W9-CGK-515

To Lily
with love
Ruby

MORE STORIES THAT LIVE

MORE STORIES
THAT LIVE

By Ruby Strand

Compiled by the Children's Division
Department of Religious Education

Reorganized Church of Jesus Christ of Latter Day Saints

Copyright © 1967

HERALD PUBLISHING HOUSE

Independence, Missouri

•

All rights in this book are reserved. No part of the
text may be reproduced in any form without written permission of the publishers, except brief quotations used in
connection with reviews in magazines or newspapers.

Library of Congress Catalog Card
No. 67 — 19042

Printed in the U.S.A.

DEDICATION

I dedicate this book of stories to all children. I also want to thank the many people who helped me write them. Sister Elva Oakman believed that I might have some talent for writing for children. Many others gave me encouragement, including my husband who shares my love for children.

RUBY STRAND

FOREWORD

For many years, Ruby (Mrs. Henry T.) Strand has written stories—many of which have been printed in *Zion's Hope* and *Stepping Stones*. In this book, we have selected and compiled many of these stories.

Young readers will enjoy the stories, and adults will find this book a ready source for a variety of themes. The storyteller will find it easy to simplify or elaborate upon the stories to make them suitable for different age groups of boys and girls. Subject indexes at the end of the book will prove helpful in selecting a story for a particular need.

Appreciation is extended to Ruby Strand for her many years of storywriting for young readers and for the opportunity she has given us to share these more widely throughout the community of our young friends.

CHILDREN'S DIVISION
Department of Religious Education

CONTENTS

8

NANCY LOVES EASTER

"Nancy! Nancy! Where are you, dear?" called her mother from the front door. She looked up and down the street but no little brown-eyed girl with yellow curls was in sight. She did see Jimmy, the smiling, redheaded boy who lived in the neighborhood. He was just turning the corner.

"Jimmy, have you seen Nancy?" she asked.

"No, Mrs. Rains, I haven't seen her," answered the boy. "I'm on my way to the flower shop for our Easter lily." His eyes sparkled with happiness. "I'm going to take it to the church, you know."

"Oh, you are? Isn't that nice!" Nancy's mother smiled.

"Yes, we've been saving pennies at our house for a long, long time. And I know some others who have, too. The church will look pretty with lots of those snowy white lilies, won't it?" Jimmy hurried on down the street, whistling happily.

Again Nancy's mother called, "Nancy!" But there was no answer.

Mrs. Biggs, her next-door neighbor and mother of Ruthie, Nancy's little friend, stepped outside just then to shake a rug.

"Have you seen Nancy, Mrs. Biggs?" asked Nancy's mother.

"Why, didn't she go over to the church with Ruthie? Ruthie went to take our lily."

"Yes, of course." Nancy's mother nodded. "How forgetful of me. I was talking over the telephone when Nancy asked. I'd completely forgotten. You say Ruthie took a lily over?"

"Yes. You know, we've been planning for weeks. The church will be so beautiful for Easter. Later the lilies are all to be taken to the Old People's Home. Ruthie is so excited. Isn't Nancy?"

"Yes, I suppose she is," said Nancy's mother. "I haven't paid much attention."

Just then a car stopped out front. Ruthie's mother went back into her house. Mrs. Rains turned to watch Nancy's daddy come up the walk. In his arms he carried a large potted lily. It was beautifully white against the waxy green leaves and fancy paper wrappings.

"Oh, how lovely!" exclaimed his wife.

"For my two girls." Daddy smiled as he set it down on the porch. "Speaking of my two girls, where is the other one?"

Mrs. Rains started to explain, but they heard voices— little girls' voices—coming from inside the house. "There they are now. They must have come in the back way," she said.

"Oh, Ruthie, didn't the church look just simply beautiful?"

"It surely did," answered Ruthie. "All those potted lilies . . . why, there must have been a hundred!"

Nancy laughed. "Not that many, Ruthie. But there were a lot of them. How I wish I had one to share."

"It's too bad." Ruthie sighed. "I know how you've been saving your pennies. Come. Let's count them again. Maybe you could buy a little one."

The two went racing through the hall and up the stairs to Nancy's room. For a while it was very still on the Rains's front porch. Nancy's mother and father were both thinking. Their little Nancy had wanted to share, and they had not helped one bit. They began to talk in low voices. They thought of a way to help Nancy to see that they understood.

Next morning the three started off to church together.

Oh, if they only knew what I know, thought Nancy. Happily and thankfully she walked along between her parents, humming softly.

"I love Easter!" she exclaimed "It's the most beautiful time of all the year!"

"Yes." Her mother smiled. "Everywhere one looks there are flowers and trees and all of nature telling us that Jesus lives."

Up the steps of the church they went through the big swinging doors and into the sunlighted room. Music—organ music and beautiful voices—came down from the choir loft above. Tall, stately, beautifully white lilies were everywhere. Nancy's heart sang for joy. Oh, I love Easter and Jesus and everyone, she thought as she followed her parents toward their seats.

And then it happened! For some reason Nancy could not quite understand she felt she must look up toward the front of the room.

"Oh!" she breathed.

There hanging above the altar was the most beautiful picture Nancy had ever seen. It showed Jesus looking right at her, smiling. His smile and his outstretched arms seemed to say, "I love you, my little Nancy." The child sat down quietly between her parents and continued to gaze at the picture. She listened to the music of the choir, sang the Easter hymns with the congregation, and bowed her head in prayer. All the while her heart was singing the joyous song, "Jesus lives. He lives in my heart today. He lives. He lives always!"

Then the minister stood up before the people. "Friends," he began, "we have met here today to talk about Jesus. He came to earth. He was hung upon the cross. He was brought back to life . . . all because he wanted to teach us the message of love."

Suddenly Nancy sat up straighter in her seat. "What's he saying about the beautiful picture?" she asked herself. "A gift from a man who doesn't want his name given? A man who has a little daughter who helped him to find the true meaning of Easter? A man who said he found Jesus living in the heart of his little girl and he, too, wanted to know him better?"

The minister went on. "The man said he felt sad to think he had believed love began and ended at home. He wants his love to reach out to all people just as Jesus' love reaches out. He wants to have love like these people who have shared their flowers."

Somehow Nancy knew in her heart that the minister

spoke of her father. And her father had bought this lovely picture as his Easter offering of love, an offering that would bring a blessing to all who worshiped there. The child could not keep back the tears because she was so happy.

Later, as she skipped along beside her parents on their way home from church, Nancy said, "I thought I had a secret. I bought a tiny lily with my pennies. All the time you had such a great big secret!"

"And the big lily I bought for my two girls was there, too," said Daddy. "It will go right along with the others to make the old folks happy out at the Home. Nancy, dear, we want you to know how very thankful we are for a daughter who has shown us how to let Jesus live in our hearts."

"Oh, I love you both so much," exclaimed the little girl. "I love Jesus, and I love everybody. Easter is wonderful!"

FROM
HER
HEART

Judy's father came home one night in April and said they were moving to another town. The girl's eyes filled with tears. To move at any time was bad enough, but to go just before Easter was very, very bad.

"We can't, we can't, we can't!" cried Judy. "Pamela and I are in the Easter service at church. We're singing a duet."

"Well, Pamela isn't moving. That will be only one to replace. I'm sorry, dear, but it's my job that takes us."

Judy reached in her pocket for a folded piece of paper. She opened it slowly. Through her tears she tried to read the song she and Pamela were to sing, but the words danced before her eyes. Her heart ached. "Now they'll ask Phyllis," she told herself, "and Pamela was just beginning to like me better."

"You'll make new friends," her mother comforted her that night as she was undressing for bed.

"I don't want new friends. I want Pamela," said Judy, crying. "Phyllis will take my place and then . . ."

Pretty soon the whole reason for Judy not wanting to move was out.

"In that case," said Mother quietly, "I think it's better if Phyllis does take your place."

"Why, Mother! How can you say such a thing?" exclaimed Judy.

"Come here, dear. Bring the slip of paper with your song on it. I want to read the words to you."

"But I know them by heart," said Judy, pouting as she lifted the paper from the wastebasket where she had thrown it angrily.

"Maybe so," said Mother, "but the words surely can't be coming *from* your heart or you wouldn't act and feel as you do." She opened the paper and began slowly reading the words of the song. Judy listened as if she had never heard them before.

Jesus died to teach us love,
Then he rose to heaven above.
May our hearts be clean and pure,
May we make our love endure.

"You see, child," her mother said in a gentle tone, "our hearts must be pure, or Jesus is not alive in us or for us."

"What do you mean, Mother?" questioned Judy.

"Why, Judy dear, can't you see that your feelings toward Phyllis are not righteous ones?"

"I . . . I . . . I guess so," stammered Judy. Judy knelt down and dropped her head in her mother's lap. It felt good to have her mother brush back her curls. It seemed to bring Jesus right into the room.   After a while she raised her eyes.

"I never thought of it that way, Mother," she said seriously.   "Phyllis is a nice girl, and she has a good voice. I can see why everyone loves her.   I'm glad now that she will get to sing with Pamela.   I guess it's a good thing I'm not going to be here.   I need to grow more loving.   Maybe next year I'll be ready to sing with some little girl *from* my heart instead of just by heart."

TRICK
OR
TREAT

Andy's daddy was a storekeeper. Andy helped in the store each day after school was out. He felt big because he was earning some money.

On the day before Halloween, Andy was all excited when he ran into his daddy's store. His eyes were sparkling.

"Oh, Daddy!" he exclaimed, "the boys and I can hardly wait until tomorrow night! We have a good trick all planned! "It's one Wally's dad used to do when he was a boy. We're going all over the neighborhood and put soap on people's windows!" He stopped to catch his breath. "So I'll just take my pay in soap today and tomorrow because I want to be sure I have enough."

He tossed his cap up in the air and caught it. "Is that ever going to be fun!"

Andy was so excited he had not noticed his father's face. He now looked up at him where he stood placing cans of food on the shelves. His father's face was very,

very serious. "Maybe I'd better get to work," said Andy. The look on his daddy's face made him feel uncomfortable. He turned away.

"Wait, son," his father said. "If that's what you're going to do for Halloween, you'd better practice up a little." He walked over to the shelf and took down a big bar of soap. "Now try this out on our store windows."

Andy did not know what to think. He just stood there.

"Go on, son," said his daddy.

Andy took the paper off the soap and walked slowly toward the front windows.

"Rub it on good and heavy," called his daddy. "Smear it on just as you plan to do tomorrow night."

As Andy went to his task, he felt foolish. "Why did I ever think this would be fun?" he was asking himself. When he had finished he went over to his father. "I'm all through," he said, his face red. "Now what do you want me to do?"

"Can't you guess?" asked his daddy, grinning.

Of course Andy knew. He was expected to wash the windows. He had done it lots of times but never when they looked like this. It was the hardest job his father had ever given him. He thought a lot as he worked. What business had Wally's dad putting them up to such a foolish trick anyway? He'd sure tell Wally. When he was about finished Wally, his pal, came in.

"Are you all set for our trick?" he asked.

"Not me!" said Andy. "I think that's a crazy idea." He explained.

"Then what *are* we going to do?" Wally wanted to know.

Andy's father had walked up to them. "Why do you have to play a mean trick on people to have fun?" he asked. "Oh, I know boys have done those things, but why? Isn't a surprise treat that will make someone happy instead of sad more fun? Isn't there someone in the neighborhood who needs the help of a couple of boys?"

"Grandma Smith!" said Andy. "She needs someone to rake her lawn."

"And help with her fall cleaning," added Wally.

"That's the idea, boys," said Andy's daddy. "What a treat for Grandma! I'm sure you'll have more fun than you would soaping her windows."

Two days later Andy and Wally sat eating Grandma Smith's freshly baked cookies. Their surprise treat was all finished, and Andy knew his daddy had been right. Real fun was doing good things for others.

Besides, he still had his money, for his daddy had said, "I won't charge you for that bar of soap you used at the store, Andy. I think it was worth the money to see my boy learning."

THE BEES WHO WERE SAINTS

Deanna brought her bike to a skidding stop and raced toward the front door of her home.

"Mom!" she called, and her voice could have been heard in every corner of the house.

"I'm right here. Don't scream," her mother answered quietly as she turned from the telephone. "That was your father. He won't be home until later. He and Brother Sherwood are driving over to Thayer to administer to a little girl who was hurt in a car accident."

"Oh," said Deanna solemnly. "I'm sorry for her. I didn't know . . ."

"That we had any church members in Thayer?" her mother finished for her. "We don't. This little girl's grandmother, who is a member, is visiting in her home, and it was she who called. What do you say we kneel and pray God's blessing upon the administration?"

Later as Deanna's mother picked up some sewing, she said, "Now tell me what caused all the excitement in your voice when you dashed in from school."

Deanna dropped to the stool at her mother's feet. "I guess it isn't too important, especially when I think of the little girl who has been hurt. I wonder—say, I wonder—"

"Wonder what?"

"I wonder if I don't already know the answer to the question I was going to ask you. You see . . ."

Soon the whole story was out. The Busy Bees, a group of girls who were all in the same church school class, had been wanting to have a Halloween party. Their sponsor, Sister Ruggles, had said, "Fine, if it makes you love Jesus more and helps you to think of Zion."

"We're having trouble, Mother," confessed Deanna. "Karen and I are the program committee, and we don't know what to do, but I think—yes, I think I have an idea." She jumped up and ran to the telephone, calling over her shoulder, "I'm going to call Karen and Sister Ruggles."

Her mother could hear bits of her share of the conversations. "Little girl—hospital—Halloween party—" flowed in from the hall.

Deanna came back to her stool with a happy smile on her face. "It's all settled," she said. "Sister Ruggles told us once that the word Halloween means 'All Saints' Day' and that long, long ago the people set aside this day to give thanks for their harvest, only they thanked a sun-god. Well, we're going to make Halloween a sharing and thanking night."

"That sounds like fine thinking," said her mother, "but how? And what? You have me very curious."

Deanna told her mother their plans. As a result of these plans eight happy girls were able to give Deanna's father a nicely wrapped package to take to Vicki, the little girl whose leg had been broken. She would have to stay in the hospital for several days. Each girl had made something the night of their party to be shared with her. They had wrapped these gifts in gay ribbons and paper. They were mostly "fun" gifts.

The extra special gift was to be opened on Sunday morning. It was a carefully planned worship service with all the words of the hymns written out, a beautiful poem composed by one of the girls, a lovely picture of Jesus bought with their own money, and a small Bible which Sister Ruggles had contributed. They had used the story of Dorcas found in the ninth chapter of the book of Acts for their scripture and had written a long letter. The letter explained how Dorcas was a saint of Bible days and that they wanted to show they were trying to be Saints of the latter days.

"You have lived up to your name, Busy Bees," Sister Ruggles told them at a later meeting. She read the letter Vicki had written them, saying she wanted to learn more about their church. "Yes," said their sponsor, "you have been Busy Bees, but you have earned the name of Saints, too—Latter Day Saints."

The words Latter Day Saints had never meant so much to these eight girls as they did now.

PRUDENCE LEARNS ABOUT LOVE

Long, long ago, when America was very, very young, there lived a family by the name of Carstad. There were Mother Carstad, Father Carstad, and a little girl whose name was Prudence Carstad. This family lived in a log house. In this log house there was just one large room. In one corner was a big fireplace. In another corner stood a big bed. This was where Mother and Father Carstad slept. Across from it in another corner was a tiny bed. This was where Prudence slept. In the fourth corner stood the table and chairs and a big, big cupboard. They called this corner their kitchen.

Now one night Prudence lay on her stomach before the big fireplace. "Crackle, crackle, crackle" went the sparks from the big logs. The little girl's eyes were bright in the firelight. "Bubble, bubble, bubble" sang the chicken soup in the big black kettle hanging over the fire. The smell of the soup made Prudence very hungry.

At that moment Mother Carstad came to stir the soup. "Ummm," said Prudence. "I wish Father would come. I am so very, very hungry."

"Father will be home soon, my child." Her mother smiled. "He has gone to the meetinghouse to get everything ready for the Thanksgiving services that we shall have tomorrow morning. He will build a fire, and after supper he will go back and spend the night there to keep logs burning so it will be nice and warm for everyone."

Prudence looked up at her mother intently. "Mother," she asked, "why does Father do so much?"

Mrs. Carstad smiled down at the little girl. "Why, I think it must be because he loves so much and is so very thankful."

Just then they heard a noise. "Stomp! Stomp! Stomp!" It was Father's boots stamping off the snow.

"There he is now!" exclaimed Prudence, and she ran to the door to greet him.

The three were soon seated at the table, and Mother filled their bowls with the steaming soup. They bowed their heads to thank God.

Several times during the evening Prudence thought of her mother's answer to her question. "Because he loves so much and is so very thankful." Even after she was lying in her snug, warm bed she was still thinking about it.

The next morning as they started out together Prudence was still thinking very, very hard. The words kept coming to her. I am glad that Father loves so much and is so very thankful, she thought. And suddenly she felt that way, too. It was the nicest and happiest feeling Prudence had ever had.

BIG
CHIEF
LEARNS

It was a bright November day. The sun shone through the open door on Teacher Ruth's kitchen floor. Johnny, her little boy, stood beside her at the table helping to pinch the edges of twelve wee piecrusts. He had counted them over and over.

"One for each of the children and one for you, Mother, and one for me."

Teacher Ruth poured pumpkin all mixed with eggs and milk and sugar and spices into the crusts and placed them in the oven. She and Johnny lived alone in a log schoolhouse with rooms in the back where they slept and cooked and ate their meals. Daddy was a missionary. He would not get home for Thanksgiving.

The log schoolhouse stood at the edge of a thick forest, and the pupils were all Indian children.

"Do you think they'll all come to the party today?" asked Johnny.

"I hope so," answered Teacher Ruth. "I have tried to tell them why we have Thanksgiving Day."

"Maybe Red Wing won't get to come." Johnny sighed. "His daddy, Big Chief, does not like the white man's Thanksgiving." Red Wing was Johnny's special friend.

"That is because he thinks the Indians' land was taken by the white men when they came to this country many, many years ago. And it was. But white men and the Indians became friends. Big Chief must forgive."

They washed up the dishes together. "Sniff, sniff" went Johnny's nose as he smelled the twelve wee pies baking. After a bit his mother took them from the oven. They were piping hot and golden brown.

"Now there is just time to go into the woods and pick some leaves to decorate the schoolroom," she said. She took Johnny's hand in hers, and soon they were scuffing through the fallen leaves.

"Oh, Mother!" shouted Johnny, "there's a tree with beautiful leaves. Look!" He reached for the lower branches.

They went on and on into the deep forest. Teacher Ruth helped fill their basket. Before long it was nearly full. They must get home. But which way was home? The tall trees with their pretty leaves were frightening now.

Johnny looked up. "Our basket is full, Mother. Let's go home. Which way is home, Mother?" His lips quivered. "Do you know, Mother?"

Teacher Ruth knelt down at his side. "We'll ask God to help us, dear." They both prayed, and Johnny tried hard not to cry.

They had just stood up when they heard a gruff voice say, "Come!"

Johnny looked up, up, up. Teacher Ruth looked up, up. There stood the biggest, tallest Indian they had ever seen. His moccasin-covered feet had come so quietly that they had not even heard him.

"Big Chief show you way to schoolhouse," he said.

"You are Red Wing's father," stammered Johnny. "Are you our friend? He says . . ."

"Hush, Johnny," spoke up Teacher Ruth. "Of course he is our friend."

They followed the big Indian chief through the forest. Then all at once Johnny shouted, "Oh, there's the schoolhouse! And there are the children waiting for us. Red Wing! Red Wing!" He ran happily toward his friend.

Teacher Ruth held out her hand to Big Chief. "Thank you, our friend, for helping us find our way back. God sent you to us."

"I see you go. I watch," said Big Chief as he took her hand and held it tightly. "I thankful for school. Red Wing learn from you, good teacher. He teach me things I not understand. I forgive."

"That is good, Big Chief," said Teacher Ruth with a smile. "You make me happy in my heart."

"I happy in heart, too," said the big Indian as he turned back into the forest. "We friends."

29

CONNIE'S POEM

It was November, and Thanksgiving was only a few days away. Connie was writing a poem to read at church school. She was having trouble.

"What rhymes with 'feast'?" she asked her big brother Bill.

"How about 'beast'?" said Bill.

Connie tried and tried, but she couldn't make a poem with that word. Then she asked her mother.

"How about 'least'?" said Mother.

That would not work either.

When she asked her daddy, he laughed. "Connie," he said, "it seems you are the only poet in this family. Maybe you will have to think of something besides eating and feasting."

Connie, stretched out on the floor in the living room, read her poem over to herself.

> I like pumpkin pie, I like dressing, too.
> I like turkey legs, I like to eat, don't you?
> That's why we have Thanksgiving,
> That's why we have a feast. . . .

That was as far as Connie could get. Just then Mother said it was time for worship. Daddy read the story of the Jaredites from the Book of Mormon. It was beautiful. "When they had set their feet upon the shores of the promised land, they bowed . . . down . . . and did shed tears of joy before the Lord, because of . . . his tender mercies over them," he read.

It wasn't hard for Connie to write her poem the next morning. Would you like to read it? Here it is:

A little child like you and me,
With ears to hear and eyes to see
A bird, a tree, the earth, the skies
Should bow his head and close his eyes
And thank our Father for his care,
Who loves all children everywhere.

THEY GAVE THEIR BEST

Every year when December drew near Mother would say, "Children, it will not be long now until Jesus' birthday. You must think very hard about what you are going to do to make it a wonderful day."

Mary Sue always clapped her hands. Benny, her brother, always clapped his hands. They loved Christmas.

This year the children began whispering together just as soon as December came. Then one night at family worship Mary Sue said, "Shall we tell them, Benny?" Her brown eyes sparkled.

Benny's brown eyes sparkled, too. He nodded happily.

Mother and Daddy listened closely. Once Mother wiped happy tears from her eyes. "Are you sure?" she asked.

Daddy asked, "Are you sure?"

Their heads went up and down, up and down.

"I'm sure," said Mary Sue.

"I'm sure," said Benny.

And that is why Christmas Eve found them all standing outside the home of Jimmy and his sister Martha. It was a shabby house with no Christmas lights in the window. In Daddy's arms was a big box. Mary Sue kept saying the words over to herself that she was going to say to Jimmy and Martha's mother when she came to the door. "We have brought these as our special gift for Jesus' birthday. Merry Christmas and God bless you."

Later as the woman took the big box and thanked them, her eyes were filled with happy tears, too.

And even though Mary Sue and Benny had given away their very own Nativity scene with the little Christ Child, they had never been so happy. After all, God had given his nicest possession, his Son. They sang Christmas songs all the way home.

A HAPPY
CHRISTMAS
EVE

When Mary Jo set the bright-red Christmas package with its silver bow down on Grandma Mills's kitchen table, she had a thankful feeling that started from her heart and made her happy all over.

Grandma Mills picked up the gaily wrapped gift and, looking down at Mary Jo, she asked, "Why, what is this, my dear?"

The little girl's pretty blue eyes shone. "It's your Christmas gift from Mother and me. You have been so good to us, and we can never show our love as we'd like to, but this will help just a tiny bit."

Grandma Mills patted Mary Jo's blonde curls, which were partly covered by a small green beret.

"Why, I haven't done very much, child," she said.

"Oh, yes, you have. Mother and I were just talking about it while we were making the cook—oh!" Mary Jo put her hand over her mouth. "There! Now I've gone and told you," she exclaimed.

34

The old lady laughed. "That *was* a slip," she said. "Don't fret about it—I still don't know what kind they are. I do thank you, child, for I know they'll be delicious." She started to untie the pretty silver bow. "You'll let me peek, won't you?"

Mary Jo had really been hoping all the time that Grandma Mills would want to open the package. She wanted to see her surprise when she first saw the cookies. She was almost bubbling over with excitement.

"It's only a day until Christmas," she answered, "so I think opening your package would be all right, don't you? And besides, there is something else in there that you just must see before tonight."

"Now I really am curious." Grandma Mills smiled as she slid the ribbon off and started unwrapping the package. On top lay a snowy-white envelope with a silver star in one corner. " 'To one whom we love so much'," Grandma Mills read.

Then she pulled back the wax paper. There lay the most wonderful looking cookies! They were in the shape of stars and sheep and shepherds and camels with the Wise Men on their backs, and there were even little manger beds.

"Oh!" gasped Grandma Mills. "The whole Christmas story is right here in these cookies!" She wiped the tears of joy from her eyes. "Thank you so very much," she added, giving Mary Jo a big hug.

"And now I must see what is inside this envelope," she continued as she opened it.

" 'Dear Grandma'," she read. " 'You are not one of my really, truly grandmas. Both of those are now living in heaven with Jesus. But you have done all the things for me that grandmas like to do, and so tonight our family wants you to share in our Christmas Eve worship service. Daddy will call for you at seven o'clock. Say that you will come, please'." The note was signed, "Mary Jo."

"It isn't very often that I go out in the evening," said Grandma, "but nothing could keep me away from your home tonight."

"We'll be seeing you, then," promised Mary Jo as she stood at the back door putting on her boots. "Good-bye."

"Good-bye, dear." The old lady waved. And then she added, "May God bless you and all kind little children everywhere who are learning the real meaning of Christmas."

Mary Jo fairly flew back home from Grandma Mills's house. Shaking off the snow from her boots, she ran breathlessly up the steps. She opened the door and called even as she began kicking off her boots and taking off her bright-green snow suit, "Mother, she's coming! Grandma Mills is coming to our worship service tonight! Where are you, Mother?"

"Here in the living room, dear," came her mother's voice. "Come, I have something to show you."

"I'll be there just as soon as I hang up my wraps," Mary Jo called back.

When she stepped into the living room, she stopped in surprise. Her mother had said she would work on plans for the worship service the family was to have that evening while Mary Jo was delivering the Christmas cookies and invitation to Grandma Mills. But Mary Jo had no idea what she was to see.

Her mother stood before the fireplace arranging figures on the mantel above. They were the most beautiful colored figures Mary Jo had ever seen. She came closer and exclaimed, "Where did you get them, Mother?" There were the shepherds in the field with their sheep. They looked almost real. And there was a beautiful star, shining as if it had been lighted in heaven. Then there were angels in glistening white robes. Mary Jo imagined she could almost hear them singing. There were wise men beside their camels. They were dressed in beautiful robes of brilliant colors. And most beautiful of all was the manger scene with the baby Jesus and Mary and Joseph. Mary Jo repeated her question. "Oh, Mother, where did you get them?"

"Daddy brought them home last night. We wanted to show them to you then but decided to wait and surprise you. Next year and the next and the next and for as many years as you are home you may help arrange these figures—you and Donnie."

Donnie was Mary Jo's little brother, who would be a year old on Christmas Day. They had all thought it wonderful that their Christmas gift the year before had been a wee baby boy. They remembered the baby Jesus, who had been born on that first Christmas Eve so many years before.

Mary Jo continued to stand before the fireplace in amazement.

"Tonight we shall turn out most of the lights. We'll have the star over the mantel turned on," explained Mary Jo's mother. "Then we shall sing the Christmas songs that you have been learning each evening all this month. Daddy will read the story of Jesus' birth from the Bible, and then . . ."

"Oh, Mother, then let's all stand and take hold of

hands, just as you and Daddy and I do sometimes, while we thank God for Jesus and all his love."

"Grandma Mills will like that, I'm sure," agreed Mother. "And we can tell our heavenly Father that we want to try harder than ever to be his helpers."

Mary Jo put her arms around her mother. "This is going to be a wonderful Christmas Eve!"

And it was, too. Everyone was happy because the real meaning of Jesus' birthday was remembered.

MARY LINDA'S CHOICE

"Oh, Mother! Look at my new piggy bank," exclaimed Mary Linda breathlessly as she dashed into the kitchen. Her mother stood at the worktable, stirring up some cookie dough.

"Why, wherever did you get it?" And then, before Mary Linda could answer, her mother asked, "And where is the baking powder, my dear?"

Mary Linda laughed and laughed. "I'll go right back and get it."

She was home again in a jiffy. "Thank you." Her mother smiled. "Now tell me about your bank while you grease these pans."

"You see," began Mary Linda, "Grandma Ross had it when she was little. Today while she was cleaning the attic she found it. She gave it to me to keep."

"Did you thank her?"

"Of course, Mother. Do you think I'd forget that?" said Mary Linda. "She had it heaping full of money at one time. That's what I'm going to do. And I'll buy . . . oh, goodness, I don't know what."

The cookies were soon baked. When she returned the baking powder, Mary Linda took a plate of them to Grandma Ross.

In the days that followed, lots of coins found their way into the piggy bank. There were many ways to save.

One day her mother said, "Linda, it's about time to get you a haircut."

The little girl thought for a bit. Then she asked, "How much does a haircut cost, Mother?"

"Plenty." Her mother laughed.

"I think I'd like long hair for a while. And if you don't mind, I'll put the money in my bank."

"We'll talk to Daddy," her mother replied.

"Certainly," he agreed. "I like your hair long." He handed her four quarters. "Clank! Clank! Clank! Clank!" They were her very first quarters. She shook the bank proudly.

"Why, there's so much in there the piggy squeals when you shake him," said Daddy. "What in the world are you going to do with so much?"

Mary Linda chuckled. "I really don't know yet, Daddy." All she knew was that it was fun to save instead of spending all her money each week for things she could so easily get along without.

And then one day on an errand for her mother, she stopped before a store window. There was the most beautiful bicycle. She knew she wanted it. She ran all the way home. "Mother," she called excitedly, "guess what? I know what I'm going to buy with my money. A blue bicycle!"

"But it will cost much more than your bank holds," explained Mother.

Mary Linda's face clouded. "Oh."

They talked about it when Daddy came home. He said, "Mother, don't you think we could help her out?"

Mary Linda ran to her daddy and hugged him tightly. "Thank you! Thank you!" she said happily.

The next day was Sunday. She could hardly wait to tell her friends. As she entered the church, soft music reached her ears. A lovely worship service had just begun.

I'll have to wait, thought Mary Linda. She sat down quietly with the other children.

The junior pastor was talking. "Christmas is not far off," he said.

And I'll get my bike, Mary Linda thought.

The pastor continued, "And Christmas is Jesus' birthday. All of us should be thinking of his gift."

As the pastor talked, Mary Linda's love for Jesus grew and grew. "What can I give him?" she asked herself. She listened carefully.

"You see, this money which we bring as a sacrifice offering will pay the way for other little boys and girls to learn about Jesus and his church and Zion," said the pastor.

Money? thought Mary Linda. Why, I have a whole piggy bank full! But, no, I can't give that. Still I do love Jesus. Oh, dear, I'm so mixed up. She could hardly wait to talk it over with her mother and daddy.

"I want to bring Jesus a gift," she explained to them, "but I want the bicycle, too. Whatever shall I do?"

"You'll work it out," said Mother, patting her hand. "We'll ask God to help you."

The next few days were hard ones for Mary Linda. As she went past the store and gazed longingly at the pretty

41

blue bicycle, she was sure she wanted it more than anything else. When friends rode back and forth to school and she saw how much fun they had, she said to herself, "I saved that money. Surely it is mine to do with as I please."

A voice seemed to whisper, "I love all little children, Mary Linda, and so many have not heard of my love." It was just as if Jesus were talking to her. Then she wanted to give all she had, and more, too.

Several days passed. One night when the little family were having their worship before Mary Linda climbed into bed, she said, "I know what God wants me to do. He wants me to think of others more than I do of myself. But Mother—Daddy—I forget when I see the bicycle."

"We'll ask God to help you decide which is best," said Mother as the three knelt down and talked to God.

The next day at school, Mary Linda noticed a new girl. Her name was Sue Ellen. They liked each other right away. Sue Ellen didn't have a bike either, and so they walked along together as they left school. Mary Linda had told her all about the money in her piggy bank and of the bicycle. When she spoke of Jesus, Sue Ellen looked puzzled. "I guess I don't know that man," she said.

"Don't know Jesus?" exclaimed Mary Linda. She couldn't believe her ears. At once she thought of the many others who had not heard of Jesus. "Now I know what I want to do," she said to herself.

That night she told her mother and daddy. "It seems to be the answer to our prayers," said Daddy.

"Why, of course," decided Mary Linda.

The rest of the week just flew along. Mother, Daddy, Mary Linda—all found ways to save. The piggy bank became heavier and heavier. Lights were turned off when no one was in a room. Water was never wasted. They found walking the short way to church was fun, and the money saved on gas went into the piggy bank. No one thought of buying candy. There were many ways to save for Jesus, and love for him grew and grew.

On Sunday morning Mary Linda learned about stewards from her teacher. "A steward is someone who takes care of something for another person," she explained. "Everything belongs to God. You are taking care of it for God."

Why, that means the money in my piggy bank, thought Mary Linda. She was happier than ever that she was learning to be a good steward.

Finally it was the night before Mary Linda was to take her offering. A newspaper was spread out on the table. She shook and shook her bank until every coin was out.

"Cling, clang. Cling, clang," went the pennies and nickels and dimes.

"Clank! Clank! Clank!" went the quarters and halves.

There was even a big silver dollar. It made a lot of noise. After a bit there were three big piles of money and one little pile. Mary Linda and her daddy counted all the money. Then Mary Linda said, "Ready, Mother. How much do you think there is?"

Mother looked up from her reading. "Let me see. I'll say six dollars."

"You're wrong." They grinned.

"Then maybe it's only about five," tried Mother again.

"More than that." Mary Linda beamed. "One more guess."

"Well, I'll say eight dollars."

"And sixty-seven cents!" sang Mary Linda, clapping her hands with joy.

Into her little red purse went the money. The purse was stuffed! She could hardly keep it fastened as she skipped along between her mother and daddy the next morning. When the offering was taken, Mary Linda dropped her coins in the basket. She looked up happily and explained, "Mother and Daddy helped a lot, so it is really their gift, too." She had completely forgotten the bicycle. All she could think of was that Sue Ellen and all the other boys and girls everywhere would know Jesus, her very dearest friend.

11

CAROL'S GOOD IDEA

We all like true stories, don't we? This is a true story of what happened in the children's department of our church in Creston, Iowa.

One Sunday morning after a very fine worship service, a girl whose name is Carol stepped up to the leader of the service and said, "Why can't we have a prayer meeting for the children some Sunday morning?"

"That's a good idea, Carol," said the gray-haired woman who was their leader. "I'll see what I can do."

That very morning she talked to Carol's father, who was an elder. "Yes, that is a good idea," he agreed. "I'll make the plans for it, and you tell all the children we'll have it next Sunday."

The word soon got around. All the children were happy. Just to make sure that everyone knew about it the gray-haired woman sent a card to each home where there were children.

When Sunday morning came, the pianist came early and played soft music as the boys and girls entered the worship room. Two boys working as deacons stood at the door to take the children to their seats. A lovely picture of Jesus with his arms outstretched was on the table in front of the room. The pastor, Carol's daddy, and another elder sat beside it.

As Carol came in quietly, her eyes grew big. This was her idea, she was thinking. And then all at once she knew that God's Spirit had planted the idea in her heart.

"And I listened and did something about it," she told herself. A good, warm feeling came over her as she thought of how God had used her to bless the children. She could almost hear Jesus saying, "Let the little children come unto me."

Carol's daddy had asked her what songs the children liked to sing, and he had used them in planning the service. The voices of the children were soft and sweet as they sang.

When the time came for prayers, many children thanked God for his blessings. Then Carol's daddy talked about the warm and happy feeling which comes when children are doing good things for people. He asked if they could think of times when they had felt God's Spirit. Of course, Carol knew all about that. Many others did, too. The time was gone before they were half finished with telling their testimonies.

"Let's have another prayer meeting," the boys and girls said. And so it was agreed that a prayer meeting for the children should be held regularly.

Because one little girl gave God's Spirit place in her heart, many children are now being blessed.

12

JANEY'S GOOD IDEA

"Zoom, zoom!" went the vacuum cleaner in Janey's house.

"Zoom, zoom, zoom," Janey was cleaning the living room rug for Mother. They were getting ready for prayer meeting. In the little town where Janey lived, the Saints gathered in the different homes for prayer meeting each week. She was so happy it was their turn.

Janey liked prayer meetings. Ever since she had been a little girl she had liked them. She loved the beautiful hymns and the soft voices in prayer. And she loved the testimonies, too. They gave her a happy feeling, and she too sometimes gave her testimony. She told the others that she always wanted to be a helper in God's church. At first Janey had been afraid. Then Daddy had explained, "They are your friends," and her fear had left.

"Zoom, zoom, zoom!" went the cleaner and then "click!" she turned it off. The rug was clean and bright.

As Janey wound the cord, the doorbell rang. It was her friend Stephen.

"Do you know what tonight is?" he asked excitedly.

"Yes, prayer meeting." Janey beamed.

"Aw, I don't mean that," exclaimed Stephen. "It's Halloween. And I'm going to have a jack-o'-lantern! Daddy got me a big pumpkin, and I want to share it with you." He talked so fast that he was all out of breath. "We'll put a candle in it and go around to the neighbors. Oh, what fun!"

That would be fun, thought Janey. She remembered last year. But last year Halloween hadn't been on prayer meeting night. "Oh, dear!" said Janey to herself.

"Well, say something." Stephen said. "Don't you want to?"

Janey answered slowly, "Of course, I want to—but—but—I wouldn't want to miss prayer meeting."

"For goodness sake!" Stephen frowned. "Aw, come on. I'm going home now. You'd better come, too, and we can have fun fixing the jack-o'-lantern." He turned to go.

It was then that Janey had a most wonderful idea. "Wait!" she called to him as she hurried into the house to talk to her mother.

"A good idea," Stephen heard Janey's mother exclaim.

Soon the children were working merrily. "Let's have queer eyes and a big, big mouth," sang Stephen.

"One that turns up at the corners, though," put in Janey. "Let's make him the happiest jack-o'-lantern in town! And, Stephen, let's have a really big surprise for everyone. We'll make him a Latter Day Saint jack-o'-lantern!"

Stephen laughed. "Is that your good idea?"

48

"Yes, and let's . . ." Janey whispered something in his ear, and soon the two were bubbling over with plans.

"I can hardly wait," said Janey.

"Oh, boy, what fun!" agreed Stephen.

That evening as soon as it was dark, and just an hour before prayer meeting time, the two children lighted the candle in their jack-o'-lantern and started out the door. They rang Stephen's own doorbell first and his daddy answered it.

"What's this?" he jumped back as though very frightened.

"Don't be afraid," laughed Janey. "This is a friendly jack-o'-lantern and he has a very important message for you."

"A message? Well, let me see it," smiled Stephen's daddy, as Janey handed him a note.

" 'Will you please come to prayer meeting tonight at eight o'clock at Janey's house?' " he read. And it was signed "Brother Jack-o'-lantern."

"A note from Brother Jack-o'-lantern. Thank you. We'll be there," he promised.

Janey and Stephen went to every house in the neighborhood. At each one they left an invitation. All the people smiled as if they thought the children had a good idea.

An hour later the living room at Janey's house was crowded with people, more than she had ever seen at prayer meeting. She felt happy in her heart.

And Brother Jack-o'-lantern, smiling proudly on the porch post, had welcomed everyone. It was a good, good prayer meeting.

13

MICKEY'S PAINT JOB

If there was anything Mickey loved to do it was paint. Mother said she was sure he would be a painter when he grew up, and Mickey said, "Yes. Help Mother paint."

The first time Mickey painted he was only two. It happened this way. Mother was painting the breakfast table and chairs. "Swish-swash, swish-swash," went her brush. Before she knew it Mickey had put his hands into the paint. "No, no, son!" exclaimed Mother when she saw blue paint all over his pretty yellow suit. There was some in his hair, too.

Then there was the time when he was four. Daddy was painting the porch swing. "Swish-swash, swish-swash," went his brush. Again Mickey wanted to help.

Daddy said, "All right, sonny. You can put on an old playsuit and paint your little porch chair." Daddy gave him a brush and a small can of paint. It was so much fun.

"Swish-swash, swish-swash," went Mickey's brush. Daddy showed him just how to do it.

When Mickey was six years old he helped Daddy paint the birdhouses. Daddy had made a lot of them. Each one had a tiny hole in it—too small for any bird but the wee wren. Even an undersized sparrow could not squeeze in, no matter how hard he tried. Mickey did a fine job.

"You're making a good painter, son," said Daddy. "The less paint you get on yourself the better painter you are. And you have just one little smear on your nose."

"Swish-swash, swish-swash," went their brushes.

And then one day Daddy said, "Some of us are going to paint God's house."

"Oh, may I help?" asked Mickey.

"Yes, I think you may." Daddy smiled. "You have learned how to do your work well, and I think we can use another good painter."

Early Saturday morning all the painters met together at the church. Pastor Jones was there and many other men that Mickey knew. Before they started work, Pastor Jones said, "We've met to do some painting for God. Shall we ask him to bless our work so that we shall do it well?" They all bowed their heads. After the prayer all the painters went to work.

"Swish-swash, swish-swash," went the brushes all the day long. There was no time to play. Everybody was busy. By the time darkness had come, God's house was all painted.

And that night when Mickey talked to God, he said, "Thank you, dear heavenly Father, for letting me help paint your house. I'm so glad I've learned to be a good painter."

14

A WONDERFUL AFTERNOON

"Hooray! Hooray! Hooray!" Cappy came running into the kitchen shouting excitedly. His mother and Brenda Sue, his sister, looked up from the dishes they were doing.

"Daddy just told me that he is taking us out to the farm to see Grandmother and Grandfather."

And then Brenda Sue jumped up and down and gave three big hoorays, too.

"Be careful there," warned her mother. "Remember you have a dish in your hand."

Brenda Sue looked down at the pretty yellow plate. "I'll be careful, Mother," she promised. "But aren't you excited?" She set the plate down with the others which she had already dried.

"I surely am," Mother agreed.

At that moment Daddy came in from the garage and found them circling about the room and shouting together, "Hooray! Hooray! Hooray!"

"What in the world is going on in here?" He laughed as he watched them.

"It's just because we are so happy," spoke up Mother. "How soon do we leave?"

"Well, I have some letters to write first," he began. Daddy was a missionary, and he was always having letters to write.

"Aw, I thought we were going right away," Cappy interrupted him.

"I did, too," pouted Brenda Sue.

"Now let's not spoil our Zionic home by putting on those ugly faces," said Mother. "I'm sure it isn't going to take Daddy too long, and I have something for us to do while he is busy."

"What is it, Mother?" questioned the children together. Their faces were all sunshiny now.

"Well, you remember we had planned to take Grandmother and Grandfather something the next time we went out to see them. We've been saving our money for quite a while."

The children ran to get the boxes in which they kept their money. They had been doing without lots of little things that they didn't really need.

As soon as they had changed clothes, the three were on their way downtown. In less than an hour they were back home again to pick up Daddy.

Grandmother said she had never had such a pretty housedress as the lovely blue one they gave her. And Grandfather's striped overalls were just what he needed. After a quick look around the farm and a romp with Grandfather's big collie, it was time to start for home.

In the pocket of each child was a surprise that Grandfather had put there.

When Cappy and Brenda Sue unwrapped their little packages, they found they each had a dime. In big letters on the paper wrapped around them were the words: "How about an ice-cream cone on the way home?"

"Hooray! Hooray! Hooray!" shouted the children.

They stopped for gas at the very first station they saw. And there were ice-cream cones for sale, too. Daddy helped them decide what kind to buy.

"What a wonderful, wonderful afternoon!" said Cappy.

"M-m-m—yes," echoed Brenda Sue, biting into her cold cone.

MOTHER'S HOLIDAY

One night after Dianne and her three brothers had gone to bed, Dianne, whose door opened off the living room, heard her mother and father talking.

Mother said to Father, "I'm so tired. All day long I've worked and worked and worked. I cooked the breakfast and the dinner and the supper. I ironed a million pieces of clothing. [Dianne did not believe there were that many pieces of clothing, but she knew that her mother really said that to mean that there were a great many.] I baked cookies and I mended and I did first one thing and then another all the day long. I'm so tired!"

"Why don't you go to visit Aunt Margaret for a week?" said Dianne's father.

"Why, George, you know I can't leave four children to take care of themselves!"

"They won't be alone. I have ten days with pay coming to me and I shall take care of them." They talked and talked and talked. Dianne tried to stay awake but after a while she fell asleep.

The next morning at the breakfast table Mother and Father told the children what had been decided.

"Oh, Mother, you aren't going to leave us, are you?" cried Ricky, Dianne's biggest brother. He was seven and Dianne was nine.

"Oh, no," exclaimed Tommy, Dianne's next biggest brother, who was only four years old. "Please stay." He left his chair and climbed up on Mother's lap, hugging her tightly.

Little David, just two and a half, sat in his high chair. He tried to say everything that Tommy did. "Mommy stay. Mommy stay," he sang.

Dianne did not say a word. All was very, very still. Then she said, "I heard you talking last night and at first I felt the same way. But now I don't. I think it's a good idea and I'll help Daddy all I can."

So it was decided. "Then I must get ready," said Mother.

All that day everyone helped to get things done. What a busy place! There were more things to do than anyone ever imagined.

When next morning came, Mother looked so pretty in her going-away clothes. Daddy looked funny because he had put Mother's apron on, and it covered only a little part of him. Daddy was a big, big man, and Mother was little. When it was time for the taxi to arrive to take Mother to the bus, everyone lined up on the front porch. First there was Father. Dianne was next, then Ricky, then Tommy, and at the very end of the row stood little David. Mother kissed each one and then she started to kiss them all over again, but just then they saw the taxi.

"Good-bye, good-bye, good-bye." They all waved until the taxi was out of sight. And then they turned to go inside. The house seemed empty without Mother.

"A whole week," said Dianne to herself. She looked at Father. He was trying hard, she could tell. "I must try hard, too."

Father smiled at Dianne. Then Dianne smiled at Ricky. Ricky smiled at Tommy, and Tommy smiled at David. Pretty soon everyone was smiling. And they just kept smiling all the time Mother was away. They knew that was what Jesus would want them to do.

16

TIMOTHY'S TERRIBLE TEMPER

Timothy Dillon had a terrible temper. Everyone knew about it—everyone, that is, except Timothy. When things didn't go the way he wanted them to, he would stamp his feet and yell loud and long. Sometimes he even screamed and upset chairs—just anything naughty he could think of— if he didn't get his own way. Timothy's mother, who was sick much of the time, tried ever so hard to help him to be a good boy, but sometimes she was very troubled about his temper.

And then one day everything changed. Timothy ran out the back door screaming, "No, no, no! I won't, I won't, I won't!" His mother called, "Come back, Timmy! Come back and eat your breakfast!"

"No, I won't!" yelled the boy. "I don't like it!" His mother was not well enough to run after him, so she turned back into the kitchen, picked up the chair the boy had upset, and knelt down beside it.

"Dear God," she prayed, "Will you please show me what to do about my boy's terrible temper? He needs his daddy so much, but his daddy is with you. Please help me. Amen."

Outside, Timmy was sitting on the garden bench pouting. No one knew he was there. Suddenly he heard voices. He peeked through the bushes. There stood Mrs. James, his neighbor, with a garden trowel in her hand. She often worked among the flowers. At her side was another woman Timmy had never seen before.

"Who lives next door?" she asked.

"Why, the widowed Mrs. Dillon and her little son Timothy," Mrs. James replied, as she knelt down and started digging in her pansy bed.

"He must be an awful child," continued the strange woman.

"No, Timmy isn't awful at all," said Mrs. James, smiling. "He's a good boy in many ways. He's a fine little helper—often runs errands for me. And I've seen him share with his playmates, so I know he's not selfish."

"I'm glad to hear that," said the strange woman. "I had decided I didn't like him one bit. I was sure he must be perfectly terrible because as I passed his house I heard him banging the door and yelling 'I won't' at the top of his voice."

"Yes. I heard him, too," said Mrs. James sadly. "It made me feel bad because people are going to forget the good things Timmy does and remember only that terrible temper."

She went on working with her flowers as the strange woman said, "It's ridiculous for him to act that way. I'm really glad I don't live near a boy who has tantrums. It might be catching." She laughed as she spoke, but a sudden fear came over Timmy. He jumped down from

59

the garden bench and walked slowly into the house. Mother stood at the sink washing dishes and singing.

The boy was surprised. Many times after he had been naughty he had found her crying. He couldn't understand. "I wonder if she knows that I have something that might be catching," he said to himself as he walked on into his room. There on his desk was a bright red dictionary. He turned to the r's. I wonder how you spell "ridiculous," he thought. He looked and looked and spelled it all sorts of ways but he couldn't find the word.

"I'll look up 'tantrum,'" he said to himself, and he had better luck that time. He found it right away but he didn't understand its meaning. Timmy was so frightened. "Maybe I'll get sick and die from it!" he cried.

Mother heard him and came running to his room. "What is the matter?"

The boy hid his face in his hands.

"Come, tell Mother," she said, sitting down on the bed and drawing him to her.

Through his sobs came the words, "The lady said I had tantrums and it's something terrible—I just know it is! She says it's ridiculous and that it might be catching and I feel sick and maybe I'll die . . ."

Pretty soon the whole story was out. Mrs. Dillon knew God had answered her prayer in a very unusual way.

She explained to Timmy what "ridiculous" meant, and that it was ridiculous to others to see a child behaving so. She told him tantrums were ugly things that took away his friends and his happiness and everything beautiful in his life. When she had finished talking, Timmy saw himself as he never had before. He was very, very sure he didn't want to have a temper or tantrums or be ridiculous ever again. He would try hard to remember.

60

17

MARILYN LOST HER SHOES

Marilyn had lost her shoes. They were her very best white shoes that she wore to God's house on Sunday. Mother and Marilyn looked everywhere for them. They looked in every room. They looked under the beds and the table and behind the doors. They looked in the corners. They looked in the closets. They looked and looked. But they could not find Marilyn's shoes.

Jimmy, Marilyn's brother who was six, looked and looked, too. He loved little sister and wanted to help. He looked outside in the playhouse. He looked in the garage and in the garden. He looked and looked and looked. But he could not find his little sister's pretty white shoes.

Daddy looked and looked and looked, but he could not find them, either.

Monday had come and gone. Tuesday had come and gone. So had Wednesday and Thursday, and then it was Friday. Still the shoes were lost. Daddy did not have very much money, and it would be very hard to buy Marilyn another pair. Those shoes just had to be found before Sunday.

On Saturday the family were sitting at the table after lunch. They were talking about the lost shoes.

"Surely we'll find them somewhere," said Mother, sighing.

"But it's almost Sunday," spoke up Jimmy. "We'll have to do something. Marilyn just can't wear those old ones." He pointed at the child's shabby playshoes.

"No," agreed Mother, "they aren't fit to wear to God's house. Oh, dear, Marilyn, can't you remember what you did with those nice white shoes?"

Little Marilyn shook her head. "They're lost, I guess. I—"

"Say," broke in Jimmy, "we've tried and tried to find them. God knows where they are. Let's ask him to help us."

"I think that's a good idea," said Daddy. "Just before lunch I was reading in the Bible that we should have greater faith."

"I know God will help us," said Jimmy. "Let's ask him right now."

The little family knelt down beside their chairs. Each one prayed. They asked that Marilyn might remember where she had put her shoes.

"And thank you, God," they added.

When they had finished, Mother said, "Now, dear, tell us. Do you remember?"

Marilyn's eyes were big and bright. "Yes!" she nodded excitedly. "I remember now. I threw them out the bathroom window!"

"The bathroom window!" Jimmy jumped up from the table. The others followed close behind. Sure enough, hidden in the tall grass beneath the window were the pretty little white shoes. They had been lying there all week.

18

DICKIE TOLD THE TRUTH

"I wonder where my hoe is," said Dickie's daddy. "I've looked everywhere for it."

"I haven't used it today," replied Mother.

They were standing in their garden getting ready to set out some fall garden plants. In a few minutes it would be time to go into the house, and Daddy needed his hoe. "I've asked Dickie to leave it alone, so I don't believe he has taken it."

"Perhaps we'd better ask him. Boys sometimes forget," said Mother. "Dickie!" she called.

Dickie was playing on the front lawn. He heard his mother and raced to the garden, his dog Spot running beside him.

"Good for you, son." Daddy smiled. "How did you ever get here so fast?"

"I flew, Daddy."

"I guess you did," said Mother. "Say, Dickie, have you any idea where Daddy's hoe is?"

Dickie knew. He knew, too, that Daddy had told him not to take it from the toolhouse. "Guess I'll tell him I don't know," he said to himself.

"But they are depending on you to tell the truth," a little voice seemed to answer.

Then Dickie said to himself, "Yes, but I'll get a scolding, and maybe Daddy won't take me on the milk route with him."

"You'd better tell the truth," said the little voice. "That is what Jesus would want you to do."

"Hadn't you better answer?" questioned Daddy.

"Yes." the boy nodded slowly. "I know where it is. I know you told me not to take it but I wanted to hoe my own little garden. The hoe you gave me isn't sharp enough."

"Where is it?" asked Daddy.

"I forgot to put it back," confessed Dickie. "I'll get it."

He ran to the little plot of ground which was his garden. There lay the hoe, and it was all rusty. Daddy's nice, shiny hoe had been left out in the rain. Dickie was so ashamed.

"You did wrong, son, to take the hoe, but we are glad you told the truth," said Daddy.

"After this I'll always try to obey," Dickie told his father. "I'm sorry I disobeyed, but I'm glad I told the truth."

Daddy and Dickie cleaned the hoe and sharpened it and Dickie's. Then they linked arms and walked into the house. Dickie felt good inside.

When they said their prayers that night, both Mother and Daddy thanked God for a boy who was truthful. And when Dickie prayed he asked God to help him remember always to obey so that he could help make a Zionic home.

19

RONNIE'S LIST

"Mother, how do you spell helpful?" asked Ronnie, tossing his pencil into the air and catching it before it fell to the floor.

"H-e-l-p-f-u-l," spelled his mother, her needle going in and out on a pair of pajamas she was mending for Ronnie. "Why do you ask?"

Ronnie grinned. "You see, it's this way. For our lesson on Sunday, each of us must have a list of ways we have been helpful. I'm trying to make my list—only—"

"Only what, son?"

"Only it doesn't seem as if I have done very much."

"Well, this is just Tuesday, Ronnie. Perhaps as the days come and go, you'll find more ways of being helpful. It sounds like a good lesson."

Ronnie exclaimed, "Oh, it is! Sister Pratt told us a good story about all the ways Jesus helped people. I surely want to be more like Jesus."

Just then there was a knock at the door. Ronnie went to open it.

"Why, it's Grandma Jackson. Come in, Grandma." said Ronnie.

The old lady wasn't Ronnie's real grandma, but everyone in the apartment house where Ronnie and his parents and the Jacksons lived called Mrs. Jackson "Grandma" and her husband "Grandpa."

"I'll step in just for a wee bit," explained Grandma. "I'm looking for a sitter. You see, I must run some errands, and Grandpa, since he hurt his foot, cannot be left alone. I was wondering—" And she looked right at Ronnie. Mother looked right at Ronnie, too. And Ronnie looked down at his paper upon which was printed "Ways I Have Been Helpful."

"May I stay with Grandpa?" he asked.

"Will you please, Ronnie? I won't be able to pay much."

"Why, I don't want any money," said the boy quickly.

And so that afternoon and many other times after school, Ronnie stayed with Grandpa Jackson while Grandma had to be away. It was such fun. Grandpa told him stories about old-time missionaries Ronnie had never seen but had heard about in church school. Grandpa had seen them and talked with them. He told Ronnie stories that weren't in the pupil's reader.

Sometimes the old man and the boy played games. Of course, the games were those that Grandpa could play while sitting quietly, but what a good time those two had! Grandpa would pretend he was someone like the missionary Paul. "Once I was shipwrecked," Grandpa would say. "I landed on an island and helped build a fire to keep warm. Who am I?"

That one was hard for Ronnie until Grandpa added, "While I was gathering wood, I had a strange accident with a poisonous snake, but the Lord did not let it harm me."

"Oh, yes!" cried Ronnie. "I know now! You are Paul." Then it was Ronnie's turn to pretend he was someone.

The man and the boy played and played until Grandpa usually said, "I'm getting thirsty. Do you suppose you could find some of Mother's good homemade grape juice in the refrigerator?"

And Ronnie always did, pouring a tall glass for each of them to sip slowly.

After that there was usually a "thud" on the front porch. "There's your paper," Ronnie would say, setting his glass carefully on the table. "I'll get it for you."

Ronnie was always made happy when Grandpa would say, "You're the best little helper I ever had. I couldn't get along without you."

And when the lists were checked at church school, Ronnie's paper was filled with things he had done to show he was learning to be like Jesus.

20

BARBARA LEARNS ABOUT LOVE

"One, two, three, four, five, six, seven . . ." Barbara counted on to twelve. "Yes, there are twelve of us and only eleven *Zion's Hopes*. What are we going to do about that, Sister Harper?"

"What do you think we can do, Barbara?" asked her teacher.

"Why, I don't know. I just have to have one 'cause I'm making a book with mine."

"I see," said Sister Harper slowly. "But surely our little guest should have one. You see, Polly has never seen a *Zion's Hope*."

Barbara had not thought of that. "Why, that is awful," she said to herself.

Every Sunday for weeks and weeks she had taken her *Zion's Hope* home. After Mother or Daddy read it to her, she fastened it into her book with the others. Often they read her favorite stories again and again.

But never to have had even *one*, thought Barbara. She looked across the room to Polly, who sat there so sure she would get one of the papers. Suddenly Barbara felt a great love come into her heart. It was such a very great love that she said happily, "Sister Harper, I don't need a paper this Sunday. I want Polly to have mine."

Sister Harper smiled down at Barbara and patted her head. "I felt sure you would want to share, my dear."

And so Barbara passed out the papers to the children. "Oh, thank you," said Polly when she was handed one. As she left for home she said, "And I'm coming again next Sunday."

Barbara had never been so happy before—no, not even when she had had a paper to take home.

21

JANE ELLEN'S SURPRISE

Once there was a little girl named Jane Ellen. She was four years old. She knew how to dress herself. She knew how to eat her egg without getting it all over her face. She knew how to brush her teeth and tie her shoe-strings. She was old enough to do all these things and many more, but there was one thing Jane Ellen could not do yet. She did not know how to read. Many times Jane Ellen would sigh and say, "Oh, dear me. I wish I could read." But she had not been to school, of course, so it was not surprising at all that Jane Ellen did not know how to read.

One afternoon something wonderful happened. Jane Ellen had had a nap and had put on a pretty red and white dress. Mother had helped her with her hair ribbon. Then Jane Ellen walked out into the living room. There sat a woman she had never seen before. Jane Ellen smiled, and the woman smiled back.

"My dear," said Mother, "this is Mrs. Norton. She is going to visit with you this afternoon while I go downtown to do some shopping. I know you are going to have a happy time together."

Somehow Jane Ellen knew they would, too, so she stood at the door waving at her mother until she was out of sight and then she turned to Mrs. Norton. "I'm your little girl now."

The woman smiled. "Yes, you are my girl for a while. Would you like to have me read to you? I brought a nice book along."

Mrs. Norton slipped a brightly colored book from her bag. It was a Jesus book. Each page had pretty pictures with some words beneath them. Mrs. Norton began reading. The book told all about Jesus when he was a tiny baby in his mother's arms. There was a picture of Mary, his mother, and Joseph, his daddy, and the baby lying in a manger bed. There was a picture of the shepherds. Mrs. Norton read all about them. She read about the angels who came to tell about the new king born in Bethlehem. She read about the Wise Men who brought gifts to the new king and about the star that lighted their way. Jane Ellen loved every picture and every word of the story.

"Please read it again, Mrs. Norton," she asked over and over.

Finally, Mrs. Norton said, "I think you could read it now, dear."

"Oh, I can't read." The child sighed.

"Just look at the pictures and try."

And before she knew it Jane Ellen was reading. She was so happy that she could hardly wait until she could share her surprise with brother Bill.

"Bill, Bill! I can read!" she exclaimed when Bill came home from school.

And never did Jane Ellen forget how to read her Jesus book. Even after she had gone to school it was her favorite book, and she read it many, many times.

22

HOW
MELVIN
DECIDED

Melvin and his brother Philip held tightly to the bright red bicycle as they looked into each other's eyes.

"You promised, Phil, you promised. You know you did, and you can't break a promise. Please let me have it."

Philip looked unhappy. "I know I did, Mel, but can't you understand? The boys are going out to the beach, and Mother said I could go, but I can't go without my bike. Won't you wait until I get home? Then I'll let you have it until bedtime. Honest Injun, I will. Come on, Bub, be a good scout."

Melvin was finding it hard to keep back the tears, even if he was seven years old. He had made some big plans, too. If I just had one of my own, he thought. No use wishing, though. Philip was eight before he got his.

The boys were still holding on to the bicycle when their mother called from the kitchen window, "Come, fellows. Get washed up for lunch. Daddy will soon be home."

Philip answered back, "Okay, Mom," and pushed the bicycle up the walk, leaning it against the porch. He walked into the house without saying any more. Melvin stopped and looked at the bike. His whole body trembled with excitement.

"If I take it now while I have the chance, I'll get to have it all afternoon," Melvin said to himself. "It would sure help out with that circus the boys and girls are having. Philip doesn't even know anything about it. I could hide from him and well . . . Still, I'm pretty hungry. I'd better eat first." His eyes were gleaming as he went into the house. A few minutes later the family was seated at the table having lunch. The boys were unusually quiet.

"What's the matter with our talking machines, Mother?" questioned their father. "Are they sick, or does a cat have their tongues?"

Their mother smiled. "I don't know, but I believe they have a problem on their hands." She turned to the boys. "How about it? Did I hear a little wrangling before lunch?"

"But, Mother—" Both boys started to speak.

"One at a time," interrupted their father. "What seems to be the trouble? Philip, you tell us."

Melvin listened as his brother explained. He was really very fond of Philip. "He's the best brother a boy could ever have," he said to himself. "Lots of boys are downright mean to their kid brothers. They don't even let them ride their bikes. But Philip is different. He does so many things for me. He's like Jesus must have been to his little brothers. And he taught me how to ride and . . . and everything."

Suddenly Melvin felt very ashamed of himself. It all sounded so different as he listened to Philip.

"It isn't that I don't want Mel to ride it," Philip was saying. "I only thought that he wouldn't mind waiting until I got back from the beach. I know I promised, and I'll stay home rather than break my promise unless he is willing to . . . to . . ."

"Release is the word you want, I think," said his daddy.

"Of course, I'll release him," spoke up Melvin. "I've been acting like a little baby." He grinned as he said it.

After helping with the dishes, the brothers walked arm-in-arm out the back door.

And Melvin was thinking, Why, I guess I'm almost as big as Philip. He felt happy all over.

23

THE TWINS CELEBRATE MOTHER'S BIRTHDAY

Douglas was fairly jumping with excitement. "Oh, I can hardly wait to tell Dotty!" he exclaimed. His face lit up as if he had just received the most wonderful gift in all the world. But Douglas hadn't received a gift. He was planning to *give* one. He and his twin sister Dotty were saving their money to buy their mother an orchid corsage for her birthday. It had all started the day their mother had admired Mrs. Warren's corsage. The twins had overheard the conversation.

"Yes, the children gave it to me," Mrs. Warren had proudly explained. "Isn't it lovely?"

"But, Douglas," Dotty had said later, "Mrs. Warren's children are big. They have lots more money than we have. And orchids cost just scads and scads and scads of money! Why, we'll never get enough."

Douglas wouldn't give up. "Let's ask God to help us find a way," he had said.

Douglas had his heart set on an orchid for their mother. He just couldn't forget the light in his mother's eyes. And now he knew how they were to get the money in those two whole weeks before Mother's birthday. As soon as he could get Dotty alone he told her how God had helped them find a way.

"You know Mr. Stowe, Dotty."

"The florist down the street where we saw the lovely orchids?" questioned Dotty.

"Yes. Well, he needs a boy and girl to help him in the mornings."

"Oh, Douglas, does he?" exclaimed Dotty. "Can we make enough for the orchid?"

"I think we'll have enough with what we've saved already, but if we don't he said he would let us have it anyway, and we could finish paying later."

The twins rose early each morning. Their eyes glowed with excitement as they did their morning chores at home and then hurried importantly down the street to their jobs.

Mr. Stowe was a small roly-poly man with twinkling brown eyes. He looked as rosy and gay as his own pretty flowers in the hothouse behind his shop.

For two weeks the twins worked hard. They helped in many ways—running errands, delivering, cleaning the shop, and watering the flowers. And the work was fun.

At last the great day came, and they counted their money. Surely, surely there was enough. Mr. Stowe counted it again as they stood breathlessly waiting to hear what he had to say.

"Do we have enough for the prettiest orchid in the shop?" asked Douglas anxiously.

Mr. Stowe smiled, and his smile spread all over his face. It bubbled over into a big laugh which made him shake all over.

"Why, you have enough and then some," he informed them.

Later the twins admired the orchid corsage pinned on their mother's dress and saw the light in her eyes as she thanked and kissed them. And when their daddy took them all out to dinner to celebrate they said, "We have the prettiest and the nicest mother in all the whole wide world."

"Thank you, God, for helping us," Douglas prayed.

"Thank you, God, for everything," Dotty prayed.

24

THE
PINK
PINAFORE

On an early summer morning many years ago, a little girl whose name was Cindy Lou stood in the parlor of her grandmother's house. Over her head she slipped the pinafore that her grandmother had finished for her the day before. It was pink, the little girl's favorite color.

"Oh, Grandmother," exclaimed Cindy Lou, "it's the prettiest pinafore in the whole wide world! I do thank you so very much for making it for me." She put her arms around her grandmother's neck and gave her a big kiss.

Grandmother smiled. "I'm happy that you like it, my dear. There's nothing I would rather do than make aprons for little girls I love. Now I must get busy and make one for your sister Patricia."

Cindy Lou looked at her grandmother in surprise. "Oh," she said. "Is Patricia going to have one, too?"

"Why, of course! I love each of you the same. But come now, breakfast is waiting."

Cindy Lou walked slowly toward the kitchen table. The pretty pink bowl from which she always ate was filled with oatmeal. The pitcher of milk with thick, rich cream stood close by. Cindy Lou was very careful as she ate, for she did not want to soil the new pinafore. Grandmother's food was always delicious, and the little girl usually ate a big meal, but this morning she seemed to have lost her appetite.

"What's the matter, child?" queried her grandmother. "Don't you feel well? I shall have to call your mother if you are ill. She would want to know."

"No, no, Grandmother," protested Cindy Lou, "I'm all right." She began to lift a spoonful of cereal to her mouth. And then she asked slowly, "Grandmother, does Patricia's pinafore have to be pink like mine?"

Grandmother thought awhile and then she replied, "No, I suppose not. It isn't Patricia's favorite color, is it? But why don't you want her to have a pink one? Come, dear. Tell me. I know you must have a good reason."

Cindy Lou hesitated, but when she saw the kindness in her grandmother's eyes she suddenly knew that she could tell her anything. Grandmother would understand.

"You see," the little girl began, "I'm two whole years older than Patricia but I'm not very much bigger, and when we are dressed alike everybody thinks we are twins."

"Why, that pleases your mother," said Grandmother, with a chuckle. "She always wanted twins."

"Yes, I know," admitted the child, "but it doesn't please me."

"You want people to know that you are older. Is that it?"

"Yes," admitted Cindy Lou. "I'm lots older than Patricia. Why, I've been to school two whole years, and she is just starting. Can't you see, Grandmother?"

Grandmother had a serious look on her face even though there was a twinkle in her eyes. "Yes, I do see, and I've just decided to make Patricia's pinafore of some pretty blue material that I have. She's fond of blue. Then everyone will know that you are not twins."

Cindy Lou jumped up from her chair and kissed her grandmother again.

"Thank you, thank you, thank you!" she said. "I guess grandmothers are the most understanding people in all the world!"

25

THE
DESK OF
HONOR

Old Ezra was eighty years old. For sixty years he had been a scribe, writing the words of God for the prophets. Every morning, just as the sun sent its warm rays down upon him, the old man went to work at his high desk. Back and forth, back and forth all the day long went his pen.

One evening after a long day's work, old Ezra sat down on a bench beneath the olive tree in his yard and said to his wife Becka, "My heart is heavy."

"Why is your heart heavy, my husband?" asked the old woman sitting beside him.

"It is because my eyes are growing dim," said Ezra. "I fear I shall not be able to finish my writing before my eyesight is gone. I am sad, Becka."

"I am sad, too, my husband. We must ask God's blessing upon your eyes."

"But I am an old, old man!" Ezra exclaimed. "God has given me good eyes for all this time. Perhaps I have no right to ask for further blessing."

"But surely it is wise to ask for this blessing. And someday God will call you to live with him, so there should be someone preparing to take your place."

The idea of a learner had been in old Ezra's prayers for a long, long time, but his grandson, named for him, liked to play more than he liked to learn to read and write.

"I'll talk to little Ezra again," he told his wife.

That night the boy came for goat's milk as he did every night. He saw his grandparents sitting beneath the olive tree.

"Greetings, Grandfather and Grandmother," he said.

"Greetings, little man," they answered back.

And then old Ezra asked, "Have you measured against the stone wall lately, my son? Seems to me that you are taller."

They walked hand-in-hand toward the wall. There were many marks upon it from the time little Ezra had been measured at two years until he was six. He stood straight and tall. His grandfather picked up a rock and made another mark on the wall. Little Ezra looked, and his brown eyes opened big and round.

"I am taller!" he shouted. "I have grown, Grandfather!"

"Yes, indeed." The old man nodded. "You've grown so tall that I wonder if you are now big enough to sit at my desk."

"But I cannot read and write, Grandfather." The little boy sighed unhappily.

"We'll take care of that," old Ezra told him. "And soon you will love God's words just as I do."

The very next morning, as the sun began to send down its warm rays, little Ezra started his lessons. Back and forth, back and forth went his pen. God blessed the old man with eyesight all the time he was teaching the boy. Little Ezra learned that there was more to life than playing all day long. He learned that the words of God were beautiful. They helped him to be a better boy.

When old Ezra was ninety years old, young Ezra was doing all of the writing for the prophets. Old Ezra could not see anymore, but that did not matter now. He could still feel the sun's warm rays as he sat under the olive tree with Becka, his wife. And he knew that God had heard his prayers. His words were being written at the desk of honor by young Ezra, the scribe.

26

HAPPY YEAR FOR PERRY

When Perry came home from school on that first day after summer vacation his brown eyes were shining. He called excitedly, "Mother! Mother! Where are you? I have something to tell you. It's something very important."

"I'm here in the kitchen, son," came his mother's voice. "What is it?"

Perry threw his cap into the air and caught it as he stepped into the kitchen, now fragrant with freshly baked cookies.

Perry did not even say "Um-m-m" as he usually did when he smelled something good. "Guess what, Mother?"

"You like your teacher?"

"I do, but that's not it."

"You got your favorite seat at school?"

"Yes, I did, but that's not it either." Perry grinned from ear to ear. "I'll just have to tell you, for I can't wait any longer."

"Neither can I." His mother smiled as she asked, "What is it?"

"I've been chosen to be a safety patrol boy!"

"Perry, how wonderful! That is something you have wanted ever since you were a small boy. How did it all happen? Wash your hands at the sink, and I'll pour us each a glass of milk. We'll have some cookies fresh from the oven, too."

They sat down at the table by the window. After Perry had taken a big drink of milk, he began his story. "You see, Miss Ely told us this morning that a boy from our room was to be chosen, but she said she did not know which one it would be. We were all given sheets of paper with a list of questions to answer."

"What kind of questions?" asked his mother, filling his glass.

Perry reached for another cookie and took a big bite before he answered. "Oh, they were important questions about obedience to law and dependability and neatness and all those things. As I read them over they looked pretty hard and I wondered if I could answer all of them."

"Then what did you do, son?"

"You know, Mother, don't you? I did just what you have always taught me to do. I thought of Jesus and his church. And I asked God to help me. Not just so I would get the job, but because I wanted to be a helper. I wanted to keep little children from being hit by automobiles. It's important, Mother."

Perry's mother had a serious look on her face. "It's important to God, too, son," she said. "He needs helpers who are reliable. And so you answered the questions correctly?"

"Yes, I did, and now I have a badge and a stop sign and a uniform and everything. I start tomorrow."

"Those are all important, too," said Perry's mother, "but the most important equipment you have is in your heart. Always remember that."

There was never a happier boy than Perry as he took his place on the corner morning after morning. Up bright and early, he could hardly wait to go. It was a happy year for Perry.

27

BABY PAUL LEARNS TO TALK

Baby Paul stood at the window looking out at the cold spring day. "Oo-o-o-o," whistled the wind.

Baby Paul listened. "Oo-o-o-o! Oo-o-o-o! Oo-o-o-o!" went the wind.

Baby Paul smiled. "Oo-o-o-o!" he echoed.

Sister Wanda looked up from her paper dolls.

"Listen, Mother!" she exclaimed. "Baby Paul is talking like the wind."

Mother smiled as she glanced up from her sewing. "He'll soon be talking like all of us," she told Wanda.

The wind whistled and whistled. "Oo-o-o-o! Oo-o-o-o! Oo-o-o-o!"

Over and over Baby Paul said, "Oo-o-o-o! Oo-o-o-o! Oo-o-o-o!" He was having lots of fun talking like the wind.

"I can hardly wait to tell Daddy," said Wanda.

Baby Paul took his nap. When he was back on the

floor again with his toys, he remembered the wind. "Oo-o-o-o!" he said and clapped his hands.

Wanda laughed. Mother laughed. Baby Paul laughed.

After a bit Mother put away her sewing. "Daddy will be coming soon," she told Wanda. "Pick up your paper dolls. I'll need your help with dinner."

Wanda was very busy cutting out a hat for one of her dolls. She answered, "Wait, Mother."

Mother called over her shoulder, "Come, dear. I need you."

Again Wanda said, "Wait, Mother."

Baby Paul smiled. "Wait, Mother," he mimicked Wanda.

Wanda looked over at her little brother. Mother had said he would be talking like all of them. She felt ashamed. It did not sound very good for him to be saying, "Wait, Mother." It was almost like teaching him to disobey. Her face was red as she put her paper dolls away. Over and over she could hear Baby Paul saying, "Wait, Mother."

"I wish he wouldn't say that," Wanda told her mother as she set the table. "Daddy won't like those words."

"That's why we must be careful," explained Mother. "Baby Paul will say what he hears us say."

Wanda suddenly had an idea. "Maybe there's time to teach him some new words," she said. She hurried to Baby Paul. "Let's pick up your toys," she told him. "Make everything tidy for Daddy."

They worked together. Each time Baby Paul put a toy into the basket, Wanda said, "Little helper."

Pretty soon Baby Paul gave a big, big smile. He clapped his hands happily. "Little helper," he echoed.

Wanda was happy. Baby Paul was learning the right kind of words.

28

RANDY FINDS THE ANSWER

This is the story of Randy, a boy just seven years old. He lived with his mother and daddy in a trailer house. All day long Randy wished for only one thing. He wanted to live in a real house.

When he was at his friend Bill's house, he thought it was the nicest house in the whole wide world. It was on a farm, and there was a barn and a haymow to play in. And when he went to bed at night, he knew the house and everything else would still be there the next morning.

When he was at Chuck's house, he decided it was the nicest house in the world. It was right across from a swimming pool, and he loved to swim. Sometimes his trailer house was in a town where there wasn't a single place to swim.

When Randy was in his own trailer house, all he could think of was that soon he would be moving. He thought about it a lot. Then he had an idea.

The next time Randy went to Bill's house he spoke

to Bill's father about his idea. "Could you give my father a job on your farm?" he asked. "If you could, then we would not have to move."

Bill's daddy laughed. "I'm afraid he would not care to be a farmer," he said. "You see, your father is an engineer. He went to college to learn how to build big bridges."

Randy sighed. "I'll ask Chuck's daddy," he said to himself.

Chuck's father was a painter. He smiled, too. "I like to paint houses, Randy. That's my job," he said. "But your father is not a painter. He is an engineer and he is doing a good work." He went on to explain that there needed to be farmers and painters and engineers and people doing all kinds of good work.

"But I want a house that stays put!" insisted Randy.

"I understand," Chuck's father agreed, as he gave him a pat on the head. "But the important thing is having a home and a family. You can have those no matter how often you move your house."

Suddenly Randy smiled. "Why, I can, can't I!" he exclaimed. "Thank you, thank you!"

Randy ran all the way home—home to his trailer house. It had never looked so nice. It was where Mother and Daddy were. It was home. It was where they prayed together and worshiped together. Now he knew that was what really mattered.

29

TRUDY
COUNTS HER
BLESSINGS

Trudy was sleeping soundly until the "crash, bang, crash!" noise awakened her. It seemed so very close. She jumped out of bed in fright.

This was the third night since they had arrived at Grandpa's dairy farm. Each night there had been disturbing noises. The first night she had run across the hall to her mother's bed. Her mother had taken her in with her and explained that the noise was only a harmless screech owl. The next night she had been frightened again. This time it was one of Grandpa's friendly mules.

And now this "crash, bang, crash!" noise which sounded as if the house were falling down.

"If it is falling down, I'd better get dressed," she told herself. Quick as a wink she was into her dress and racing across the hall. "Mother! Mother!" she screamed. "The house is falling down!"

But Mother's bed was empty. Trudy stood still for

a moment. Again she heard the noise. "Crash, bang, crash!"

She ran to her brother Timmy's room. He was older than she and was not the least bit afraid. He had visited the farm before. Timmy's bed was empty.

"Where is everyone?" she called anxiously as she rushed down the stairway and into the kitchen. She stopped, out of breath.

Mother stood at the window. She turned. "Good morning, dear," she said. "You are just in time to . . ."

"Mother! The house is falling down! I heard . . ."

Before she could finish the noise came again. "Crash, bang, crash!"

Mother smiled. "See," she said, pointing.

Trudy looked out the window. And then she knew. There in the driveway stood a big yellow truck. A man was loading cream cans into it. "Crash, bang, crash! Crash, bang, crash!" Can after can went into the truck.

"Did you forget that Grandpa said the cream truck would be here this morning?" Mother asked Trudy.

"Oh, yes, I did," Trudy answered, "and I was scared. Mother, let's go back to the city. I want Daddy to come home and I want our own house where there aren't scarey owls and mules and everything."

"That is impossible right now, dear," said Mother. "Daddy is one of God's helpers, and he is telling people of other countries about God's church and about Zion. We must be thankful we have a daddy who can do this."

Trudy began to cry. "But, Mother . . ."

"Wait, dear. Let's stop and think of how many blessings you have. Grandpa is lonely here since Grandma went to live with God. Until he sells the farm, we are needed here. It is a blessing that we can help him."

Trudy was still crying. "But . . ."

Mother went on, "Besides, don't you remember how the doctor said a year on the farm was just what you needed after your sickness?"

"Yes, but . . ."

"That makes three blessings. You'll get strong like Timmy and be able to help Grandpa a lot. What a lot of blessings!"

"But the noises, Mother!"

"You'll soon learn to like them," promised Mother.

Just then Grandpa and Timmy came through the back way.

"Those are pretty smart cows we've got, Tim," Grandpa was saying.

"How much money did the cream bring, Grandpa?" asked the boy.

"Enough to help buy that pony for you and Trudy," Grandpa answered with a grin.

"Hooray!" shouted Timmy.

"A pony!" exclaimed Trudy. All at once she liked the farm. She believed she would soon like to be awakened by its many country noises. She knew she would like the sound a pony made. "Why, a pony will be another blessing!" She smiled up at her mother.

"Yes." Mother nodded. "We must always count our blessings."

And as they sat down to breakfast, Trudy said, "May I say the thank-you prayer, please?" Trudy's heart was full of thankfulness.

30

HUNDREDS OF HOUSES

Jackie lived with his father and mother in a small town in Illinois. Jackie's father was a carpenter. He had built houses. He had built stores. He had built churches. But now Jackie's father could do none of these because he was crippled and sat in a wheelchair. He was very unhappy because he could not build houses and stores and churches. "If I could just do *something* with these hands," he would say.

One beautiful spring day in April Jackie came home from school and found the unhappy look on his father's face. It made him sad, too. He wished there was something he could do to help. He often prayed about it.

Then a most wonderful thing happened. Jackie had started out to play just as he heard the doorbell ring. He opened the door. There stood two strange men. One man was tall and thin. He had a friendly smile. The other man was short and fat. His eyes were twinkling.

"Hello, sonny," said the tall thin man.

"I'm Mr. Smith, and this is Mr. Jones. We're from a big store in Chicago. Is your father a carpenter?"

Yes, but . . . but . . ." began Jackie.

"We know, we know," said the short fat man whose eyes twinkled, "but we think we have just the job for him. By the way, are you a carpenter, too?" He gave Jackie a friendly pat.

"I used to help my daddy a lot," the boy answered proudly.

"Fine, fine. May we come in and talk to your father?" asked the tall thin man.

"Oh, yes," said Jackie. To himself he was thinking that God was answering his prayers. He hadn't known how God would make his father happy again. He had just prayed that he would. He was so excited that he forgot all about going out to play.

"Mother! Daddy!" he called, leading the two men into the living room. His mother laid down her sewing, and his daddy looked up from his reading. "This is Mr. Smith and this is Mr. Jones. They want to talk to you, Daddy."

The two men sat down. The tall thin man explained their errand. "As you know, this is April, and May will soon be here. The birds are returning from the south. Soon there will be lots of boys and girls coming into our big store in Chicago. They'll be wanting to buy birdhouses. Can you make them for us?"

Jackie watched his father's face. The unhappy look disappeared. A happy grin came to take its place.

"I'll say I can," he said. "That is, I can with Jackie and Mother's help. I've been wishing for something I could do."

"Good," said the short fat man. Then they talked over all the plans.

"How many do you want?" asked Jackie's father.

"As many as you can make," said the tall thin man. "How about five hundred?"

Jackie's father smiled until all the frown wrinkles left his face. He nodded his head and then he said, "Hundreds of houses!"

Jackie clapped his hands. "We'll have fun making red houses and blue houses and green houses—and every color."

Later that night, as he knelt beside his bed, he talked to God about this wonderful thing that had happened. "Thank you," he prayed, "for making my daddy happy again."

31

THE STORY OF THE LOST PURSE

Jimmy and Lonny went running toward their mother, who sat watching the children at play in the park. They called excitedly, "Mother, Mother, look what we found!"

All out of breath Jimmy held up a little girl's pretty red purse. "See?"

Lonny added, "And there's a lot of money in it. We took a little peek to see."

Jimmy, who was older and knew how to count money, explained that there were eighteen pennies.

"We must try to find the child who has lost it," said Mother.

"I saw a little girl with long braids leaving the playground when we first came to play, and she was crying," said Jimmy. "Maybe it was hers."

"Where did you find it?" questioned Mother.

"In the tall grass," answered Lonny.

Jimmy explained further, "I was hunting my ball down by a bush when I found it."

As they were talking their daddy came back. When they showed him the purse he said, "We'll watch the 'lost and found' column in the newspaper."

The boys knew what that meant, for they had lost their pet dog Perky and the newspaper had helped them find him.

In the days that followed all sorts of lost things were advertised. But there wasn't a word about a pretty little red purse with eighteen pennies, a handkerchief, and a mirror in it.

"Does that mean that we may keep it?" questioned Lonny. He was already talking of how much money they'd have to spend.

"No," his mother told him. "I think we'd better put an ad in the paper. Whoever comes may get the purse by paying what the ad costs us."

One whole day passed and then another and then it was Sunday. As they were coming home from church they noticed a strange car parked in front of their house. Jimmy knew right away that the little girl sitting in the back seat was the one he had seen in the park.

Her daddy got out of the car and came toward them. "We have come for the purse," he explained, looking toward the boys. "That was an honest, upright thing to do." Then he held out a dollar bill. "This is your reward."

"We'd rather have the money in the purse," spoke up Lonny.

All the big people laughed, and Lonny looked surprised. Even Jimmy grinned.

Finally everything was taken care of. Lonny ran in

for the purse. Nancy, the little girl, smiled happily to see it again and shared her pennies with the boys. Her father paid for the ad and almost insisted that they take the dollar bill also, but Jimmy shook his head.

"We don't want our boys to feel that they must be paid for doing the honest things," Daddy explained. Nancy's father told them God needed lots of boys like them.

That night when the boys and their parents had their family prayers they had many happy things to tell God.

32

GOD
IS
WONDERFUL

Jeani sat at the breakfast table finishing her cereal. "Mother, what did you call those flowers that started blooming in our garden yesterday?" she asked, looking up at her mother.

"Canterbury bells, dear," answered her mother, as she cleared the table. "And please hurry. We must be getting ready for church school."

"Canterbury, Canterbury, Canterbury," sang Jeani between bites. "I can remember the 'bell' part but 'Canterbury'—"

"It is quite a long word," her mother agreed, taking her empty bowl. "Scoot now and brush your teeth. I'll finish tidying up the kitchen and then I'll comb your hair. Daddy will be saying it is time to start before we know it."

Jeani repeated the word Canterbury several times as she was getting ready, and even as they left the house she was still saying it.

"Why are you so interested in the word?" queried her father as they were getting into the car.

Jeani explained. "Our teacher, Miss Anne, asked each of us in our class to have a true story ready for today which would tell something about God's love. I want to tell about the Cant—Cant—"

"Canterbury," spoke up her father.

"Yes. Oh, I do hope I'll remember to say it right."

"Tell me the story," suggested her father. "I haven't heard it. Wouldn't you like to practice telling it as we ride along?"

It was a lovely June morning, and hardly any traffic had begun to rumble along the highway.

Jeani settled more comfortably between her mother and daddy in the wide front seat.

"I'd like that," she said. "It was yesterday morning, and Mother told me when I got up that the Cant—Cant—Canterbury bells were blooming. I looked out the kitchen window, and there they were, standing so straight and tall and blue. As I looked at them I suddenly heard a bell-like sound. I said to Mother, 'Why, they're ringing, too!' "

"Jeani was right in thinking so," her mother interrupted. "There was a little wind yesterday morning, and the flowers were nodding in the breeze. It did look and sound as if they were ringing—but go on, dear."

"So I opened the door very, very quietly," continued Jeani, "and I tiptoed down the path. I stopped right beside them. 'They are ringing!' I told myself. And then I saw a beautiful soft brown bird, a little bit smaller than a robin. It was marked with black and yellow beneath. Its tail was black, and its throat was yellow, and there was a patch shaped like a moon on its breast. Mother later told me it was crescent shaped. I looked more closely and I saw a nest made of grass right there on the ground. I was never so close to a bird and its nest before."

"A meadowlark!" spoke up Daddy. "And he was ringing the bells on the Canterbury stalk!"

Jeani laughed. "I thought so at first."

"And she came running toward the house calling to me," her mother said, laughing.

"Well, that is the most amazing story I ever heard," spoke up her daddy. "I never heard of a meadowlark smart enough to ring the bells on a Canterbury stalk. I know your class and your teacher are going to like your story."

"And I know you are teasing me, Daddy," Jeani answered.

"Oh, is there more?"

"Indeed there is. You see, he came back, and this time I knew the bells hadn't been ringing. It was his bell-like singing that I heard. His wife and the little family of birds were out there, too, and he was telling everyone about them. My—God is wonderful!"

"Indeed he is," agreed her father. "And if I were you I wouldn't worry if I forgot the name of the flowers. The important thing is to remember always that God is truly wonderful. You'll have a fine story to share with your class this morning. It's a story of God's great love."

33

A SABBATH STORY

(Jesus and His Friends)

Joshie, a little Jewish boy, followed Jesus and his twelve helpers through a cornfield on a Sabbath day long, long ago. He saw the tired look on the men's faces as they went pushing along through the tall grain. Plod! Plod! Plod! went their feet, for they had walked a long way. He heard the helpers talking quietly among themselves, and then Peter saying to Jesus, "Master, we are tired and hungry. When shall we eat?" Joshie saw the kind look on the face of Jesus as he answered, "The traveler has always the right to eat of the ripened grain in any field."

But it is the Sabbath! Joshie thought. Surely Jesus would not let them pick corn on the Sabbath! For Joshie, being a little Jewish boy, knew that it was breaking the law to do any kind of work on the Sabbath. But there before his eyes he saw them picking and eating the grain. Joshie loved Jesus very much and decided that he was a wise person. He said to himself, "Surely it is not wrong to do such a thing when they are so hungry and tired. Jesus always knows best."

And then suddenly he heard a noise like the roaring of many lions. He looked up in fear. "Those mean scribes and Pharisees!" he said to himself. "They are always scolding Jesus." He would never say this aloud, for these men were the fear of all children.

Joshie hid among the tall stalks of corn and peeked out, listening closely. Sure enough, Jesus was being scolded. He did not seem to mind, however, and answered softly, "The Sabbath was made for man, not man for the Sabbath."

Joshie followed slowly behind as Jesus and his helpers continued their journey, and he said over and over to himself, "Jesus is right. Jesus is right. He is always right. And when I reach home I'll tell Mother just what he said: 'The Sabbath was made for man, not man for the Sabbath.' She will understand."

34

A
SABBATH
HEALING

(Jesus and His Friends)

Joshie followed Jesus many times, for he loved him more than anyone in the whole world. And so, on another Sabbath day, he was one of the many people crowding near him, listening to his wonderful words. Joshie followed Jesus into the synagogue where he taught and talked about God. This time Joshie's father was with him, and Joshie whispered to him, "Oh, it is wonderful!" There were tears in his eyes, happy tears, because he loved Jesus so very much.

And then a man drew close to Jesus. One arm hung limply at his side, and the hand was withered like a dried prune. The man spoke pleadingly, "Lord, my withered hand. See it? I cannot work for my family as other men. Can you make it well?"

"Of course Jesus can," Joshie said to himself. "But will he?" He watched Jesus as he heard the low, angry voices of the scribes and Pharisees: "He dare not! He dare not! It is the Sabbath!" they shouted.

"But he will dare," Joshie whispered to his father. "Remember how he said the Sabbath was made for man, not man for the Sabbath?"

"Ah, child," his father whispered softly, sighing as though very troubled, "I fear for Jesus."

But Jesus seemed to have no fear. He beckoned. "Rise up and come close," he called to the man. He looked right at the angry scribes and Pharisees. "I will ask you one thing," he said. "Is there anything wrong in doing good deeds on the Sabbath? Should we not save life on every day?" And then, looking straight into the face of the man who was crippled, he said, "Stretch forth your hand." The man obeyed.

And the most wonderful thing happened right there before everyone's eyes. The man's hand was made well! It looked just like the other one.

The scribes and Pharisees were as angry as could be. They muttered and grumbled and shook their fists at Jesus.

Joshie felt sad in his heart because they did not love Jesus as he did. And as he took his father's hand and walked slowly toward home, he promised himself he would be a better boy so God would know how very thankful he was for Jesus, who was his dearest friend.

35

A
GREAT
STORM

(Jesus and His Friends)

It had been such a busy day for Jesus. All the day long he had gone about doing good. An old woman, Peter's wife's mother, had been very ill, and he had healed her. She had been able to rise from her bed and prepare a nice meal for Jesus and his helpers. And then, when he had left the house, there were the hundreds of people waiting for him. They had followed him all the day long. He had healed the sick, caused the blind to see, and made the lame to walk. Jesus was happy that he could do this for them, but now he felt that he had to rest for a while. He turned his eyes longingly toward the sea where a ship was anchored.

"Let us take the ship across to the other side," he said to his helpers.

They walked toward the seashore. Many followed, but gradually the multitudes of people thinned out.

Jesus slipped into the ship, and his helpers found

their places near him. The sea was peaceful and calm. Jesus sighed as he said, "Ah, how restful." John, the beloved helper, found a pillow for Jesus' head, and soon he was fast asleep. The soft wind cooled him as he slept.

Peter and James and John and the others talked quietly of their Lord. Then they noticed that the wind was blowing harder. Harder and harder and harder it blew. Big waves swept up over the ship. Splash! Splash! Splash! they went. The helpers' eyes opened wider in fright. They looked at Jesus still sleeping.

"How can he sleep with so much noise?" asked Peter.

And then, just as the wind howled noisily and the waves splashed up over him, Peter exclaimed, "Master, we are having a terrible storm!" He shook Jesus until he was awake. "Can't you see that we shall soon be drowned? What shall we do? What shall we do?"

Jesus looked at Peter and the other helpers. Then very softly he spoke. "Where is your faith, my friends?"

Gently he spoke to the sea just as if it could hear. "Peace, be still," he said. That was all.

The helpers watched as the wind stopped blowing and the waves ceased splashing into the ship. All was calm and still. They turned to each other, their faces showing wonder.

"Why, even the wind and the sea obey him!" gasped Peter. "What kind of person is this?"

"He must be the Son of God," answered the others.

36

A LITTLE GIRL IS HELPED

(Jesus and His Friends)

Jairus looked sad. He looked very, very sad. Jairus' wife was sad, too. Their little twelve-year-old daughter was ill. She was very, very ill. They had tried to make her well. They had lots of money, for Jairus was a ruler in the synagogue. He had called in the doctors and learned men, but the little girl lay on her bed crying all the day long because she felt so sick. Jairus sat at her bedside holding her hand. The child's mother sat there, too, pushing back the soft curls from her hot forehead.

"Oh, if there were only someone who could make her well," they whispered to each other.

Finally Jairus stood up. He turned to his wife, "I am going to that man Jesus that everyone is talking about. Our friends in the other room say he is in town today."

"You have waited too long," said the little girl's mother, sighing. "Can't you see that she is now past helping? Oh, if you had only gone when she first asked you!"

"I know. I know," her husband admitted. "I know I have been stubborn and have spoken unkindly of him many times, but if he will come and make her well, I shall be his follower always."

"Go then," agreed his wife, "though I fear it is too late." She brushed the tears from her eyes as she watched the slow breathing of the child.

Jairus left the room, and she sat alone with her little girl. The child lay still, so very still. The mother got up from her chair and went slowly out the door to the many friends who were waiting. Walking up to one, she said, "Go and find my husband. Tell him that it is too late."

Immediately there was much crying and talking among the friends. The mother went back into the room and closed the door. And then suddenly she heard a strange voice. It sounds like music from heaven, she thought.

She went to the door and opened it. There stood a man she had never seen before, but as she looked into his kind face something seemed to tell her it was Jesus.

"The little girl is not dead," he said.

She heard the people laugh at him. But he entered the door of the room where the little girl lay.

Jairus and his wife watched as he came close to the bed. And then he spoke in the same kind, gentle voice, "Little girl, I say unto you, arise."

With questioning eyes Jairus and his wife saw the child get up from the bed and look around. She knelt at Jesus' feet, and they hurried to kneel beside her.

Jesus patted her head as he spoke: "She is well and hungry. Give her something to eat."

Never had anything so wonderful happened in Jairus' home. "We shall be your followers all the days of our lives," Jairus and his wife promised.

110

37

A LITTLE
BOY
SHARES

(Jesus and His Friends)

Tramp, tramp, tramp, went the feet of Jesus up the mountainside.

Tramp, tramp, tramp, went the feet of his twelve helpers up the mountainside.

Tramp, tramp, tramp, went the feet of many, many people up the mountainside.

Among these many people was a small boy. In his hand he carried a basket in which was the lunch his mother had fixed for him.

"You will be hungry if you stay all day," she had explained. "Here are five small barley loaves of bread and two wee fishes. Remember, the day is long. Do not eat before you have reached the top."

Eagerly he trudged along behind the others, trying to edge his way closer to his hero, Jesus. Tramp, tramp,

tramp, went his feet up, up, up the mountainside. Finally they reached the very tiptop. The cool green grass felt good on the little boy's tired feet. He watched Jesus sit down. Then he watched Peter and Andrew and James and John and Philip and the other helpers sit down. He found himself near Andrew. He was happy about that because Jesus was not very far away.

The boy listened closely as Jesus talked. "I'll listen to every word so I can tell Mother and those who did not get to come," he said to himself.

After awhile he noticed Jesus motioning to Philip and heard him ask, "Where may we get bread that these people may eat?"

Philip answered, "We have only a small amount of money. It is not nearly enough to buy bread for all these people."

The little boy looked down at the basket at his side. Oh, how I wish I had enough to share, he thought. Well, it will help a little, he decided. He whispered to Andrew, "I have my lunch. There are five small barley loaves of bread and two wee fishes. I'd like so much to share them."

Andrew laughed as he called to Jesus, "There is a lad here with five barley loaves and two small fishes." Again he chuckled as if it were a good joke.

But Jesus did not laugh. He beckoned to him to bring his lunch and made room at his side for the boy.

Never in all his life had the little boy felt so happy. He heard Jesus say, "Ask everyone to sit down." He watched all the people, nearly five thousand of them, find places to sit. The ground was covered with people. Something wonderful is going to happen, he thought, as he watched with big round eyes.

112

Jesus took the loaves and lifted his eyes to heaven. "Dear God," he prayed, "bless this bread to all these people, and thank you." Then he passed the basket among the helpers, and there was plenty for them. The little boy could hardly believe his eyes.

Jesus asked the men to pass the bread to all the people. As the little boy reached for his piece, he felt his eyes fill with tears.

Then Jesus did the same thing with the two wee fishes. There was enough food for everyone. Even more wonderful was that there were twelve basketfuls over. "Gather up what is left," Jesus had said, "that nothing is wasted." And then he had looked down at the boy and smiled.

When the people started for home, the little boy felt as if his feet hardly touched the ground. "How can I ever tell them so they will believe me?" he kept asking himself. "Oh, but it is true. It is true! I shall follow Jesus always!"

38

A WALK WITH FRIENDS

(Jesus and His Friends)

Far, far away, and long, long ago, there were two men walking along a dusty road on their way to the little town of Emmaus. Their faces were sad, for only a few days before they had said good-bye to Jesus, their very dearest friend. "We'll never see him again," they said, and sighed as they tramped along.

Suddenly there appeared a man in the road. The man could see that they were very sad, and so he asked, "What is your trouble? Why are you so unhappy?"

"Surely you have heard," spoke up Cleopas, one of the men.

"Heard what?" questioned the stranger.

"Why, about Jesus of Nazareth. He was our very dearest friend. He was so kind and good, and he helped us to know God better. He taught us many things. And now he is gone. The wicked men have crucified him."

114

"And as if that were not enough," spoke up the other one, "there have been stories told about that he is alive. We just can't believe those stories. Ah—our hearts are so heavy, for we saw him on the cross."

The stranger had listened closely as they talked. "And why not?" he asked. "Surely you recall that the good men of old, the prophets, said that Jesus would rise again."

As they walked along he told them many things which caused them to stare in wonder. Soon they reached the little town of Emmaus. The stranger started to leave them.

"No. Come with us," they invited. "It is almost dark, and we will see that you have a place to eat and sleep."

The stranger walked along beside them. Soon they sat down to a table of food. The stranger took bread and blessed it, then offered some to each. And then the most wonderful thing happened! As they took the bread the men really looked at the stranger for the first time. Before their heads had been bowed in sadness.

"Jesus!" they exclaimed together.

Yes, surely enough, it was Jesus. And as quietly as he had shown himself, he now quietly disappeared.

"Why, we've been talking with Jesus!" They almost sang their words. They did not look unhappy now.

"Jesus is alive! We know it. We will never doubt again."

Away they went to tell the news to Jesus' other friends.

39

ON
THE
SEASHORE

(Jesus and His Friends)

It was a very warm spring afternoon, almost like summer. Peter and James and John and the other disciples walked slowly down the path which led to the seashore. It had been lonely since Jesus had gone away. Finally Peter said, "I'm going fishing."

"We'll go with you," said the others.

They went down to the seaside and climbed into a ship which was anchored there. All the night long they fished, throwing their nets into the blue, blue water. The boat rocked and swayed and swayed and rocked all through the dark night. When morning came their net still had not a fish in it.

Suddenly they saw a man standing on the shore. He called out, "Throw your net out on the right side of this ship and you will find lots and lots of fish."

They did just as the man told them to do, and the

net was so heavy that they had to pull and tug and tug and pull.

"Who is this man who knows so much?" they said, looking again more closely.

Then John excitedly exclaimed, "Why, it is Jesus!"

They hurried to shore, dragging the net of fishes— that is, all but Peter, who jumped into the water and swam in.

Jesus had a cheery fire burning and fish frying over the coals. Closer and closer came the hungry disciples. Jesus had bread ready, too, and he called to them, "Come and eat."

The men drew nearer and nearer with surprise in their faces. "How could it be?" they asked themselves. This was the third time that Jesus had shown himself since he had risen from the tomb. They knelt and ate of the good breakfast which Jesus had prepared. When they had finished, Jesus called Peter closer to him. "Do you love me more than you do your fishing?" he asked.

Peter answered, "Why, you know I love you, Lord."

"Then feed my lambs," said Jesus.

Peter immediately thought of all the little children who did not know of Jesus and his kindness.

Again Jesus spoke. "Do you love me, Peter?"

And Peter replied as before—"You know I love you, Lord."

"Then feed my sheep," said Jesus.

Peter sat thinking of the many, many people who did not really know his friend. Then he heard Jesus ask again, "Do you love me, Peter?"

For a moment Peter was hurt. "How many times is

he going to ask me?" he said to himself. Aloud he answered as before, "Lord, you know that I love you."

Jesus repeated. "Feed my sheep."

And Peter did not forget. He and his friends went from place to place telling the children and the mothers and fathers about Jesus and his wonderful love.

Peter remembered to tell his friends about Jesus. Do you remember to tell about Jesus, too?

40

JESUS GOES AWAY

(Jesus and His Friends)

Peter and his friends sat together in an upper room talking of Jesus. "I wonder if he will come again today?" they asked one another. "Can he really be alive or could we have dreamed it all?"

Suddenly the door was opened and there stood Cleopas and his friend. They had returned from Emmaus in great haste. Breathlessly they exclaimed, "Jesus is alive! Jesus is alive!"

"Yes, Jesus lives," repeated Cleopas. "We saw him. We ate with him."

"At first we did not know him," Cleopas' friend continued, "but suddenly our eyes really saw, and we knew it was Jesus."

Peter and the other disciples said nothing. So many wonderful things had happened that they could not find words with which to speak.

And then another voice was heard. They all looked up. There was only one person with a voice as kind and soft as this. The men looked very, very frightened. Every time it was like this. Somehow it was hard to understand that Jesus was really alive.

"Why are you afraid?" asked Jesus. "I am not a spirit. Come, it is I, Jesus. A spirit does not have flesh and bones as I have."

They still looked unbelieving, so he asked, "Do you have any food? I will show you that I am alive even as you."

They hurried to find food for him. "Here," said Peter. "Here are broiled fish and golden honey." As Jesus ate they watched.

He was alive!

"Come, follow me," he beckoned when he had finished eating. Jesus led them to a hillside near the little village of Bethany. "I will tell you many things."

And Jesus did tell them many things. His friends listened closely as they learned of the work they were to do. Not once did they take their eyes off his face. Jesus told them that no matter where they were his Spirit would be with them to guide and help them if they were telling others the gospel.

When he had finished Jesus blessed them for the work they were to do and then—slowly, slowly, slowly— he was taken up into heaven to be with God.

"We are alone," they whispered. "No, not alone," they added. "His Spirit will be with us always."

All at once they did not look sad anymore. Their faces were shining with happiness, and they smiled at one another as they started back to Jerusalem.

41

AT
THE GATE
BEAUTIFUL

(Jesus and His Friends)

"Come, John, let us go up to the temple and pray," said Peter, the apostle.

"That is a good idea," agreed John. "If we are to help Jesus with his work now that he has gone back to live with God we will need to pray often."

"Tramp, tramp, tramp" went Peter's feet on and on toward the temple.

"Tramp, tramp, tramp" went John's feet on and on toward the temple.

Finally they reached the Gate Beautiful. Just as they started to enter through the gate they heard a voice. There on the ground lay a man.

"Give me some money, please," he said. "I am lame. I have been like this since I was born, and every day someone carries me here where I can beg for money to buy my food."

Peter and John looked down at the man. They looked as if they would like to do something, but they did not have any money. What could they do?

Then suddenly Peter turned to John and whispered something. "If he could be well he could work for his money," Peter had said.

"Look on us," they said out loud together.

The lame man looked up expectantly. "You are kind men," he said. "I wonder how much they will give me," he said softly, almost to himself.

But instead, Peter, the older of the two apostles, said, "I have no silver or gold."

The lame man turned to John. "Is it you who has money? he asked.

Then Peter spoke again. I'll give you what I have. In the name of Jesus Christ, rise up and walk."

Peter took the man by the hand and lifted him up. Immediately the man's feet and ankle bones became strong. It was a miracle!

"I can walk! I can walk!" he said eagerly, leaping up and down in great joy.

Peter and John smiled in happiness, too, as they walked slowly through the gate and into the temple. The man who had been lame and could now walk followed. "I want to praise God, too!" he cried, his eyes shining. "You have given me something far more wonderful than money."

42

FEAR NOT

(A true story)

The huge ocean waves swished and swashed against the shore of a little island village. Darkskinned men and women and boys and girls waited eagerly for the ship they could see drawing nearer and nearer. On it were their dear friends, Brother and Sister Joseph Burton, who had been missionaries to their land and were now returning for another visit. The Burtons had told them all about Jesus and his church. No wonder the natives could hardly wait to see them.

"Swish and swash, swish and swash" went the waves. "It won't be long now," they seemed to say.

As the ship slipped in toward shore and they greeted their friends, these darkskinned people thanked God in their hearts for bringing the Burtons safely. The natives knew God loved all people and that the color of their skins made no difference to the great All-Father.

One of these native sisters was a leper. By now she should have been sent away from the others who might catch the disease from her. She was such a kind woman, however, and everyone loved her. She had a beautiful voice and sang for the church services. Her friends knew they would miss her and she would miss them. As yet nothing had been done about sending her away. One Sunday morning as she came into the church, she chose a seat next to Sister Burton.

"Oh, dear," said Sister Burton to herself. "I hope I don't get her disease." Suddenly Sister Burton became very, very frightened. The beautiful singing of the service came to her ears, but she could not worship. All she could think of was this dreaded disease. What if she should get it! She thought of herself as a leper, separated from her husband and family and friends. Why, how could she serve God in his church if she were a leper? He was depending upon her to help others who were ill. Many times she had sat at the bedside of the sick and comforted them. "No, please, God," she prayed.

At the other side of her stood her husband, Brother Burton. When the singing was finished and they had settled themselves in their seats, he whispered to her softly, "My dear, I do not know what this means, but while we were singing God said to me, 'Tell her it shall not harm her.'"

Sister Burton looked happily up into her husband's face. "I know what it means," she said.

Later, at home, she told him all about what had happened, and they knelt together to thank God for this wonderful promise. Her fear was gone. "I will trust and not be afraid," she said.

Many times, in her loving care of the sick, she thought of this experience and never, never did she catch any disease in her work. God was true to his promise.

43

A DANGEROUS WISH

(A true story)

"Oh, but it's a scorcher today!" exclaimed Brother Joseph Burton, the beloved missionary of long ago.

"Yes, too hot for a four-mile hike," agreed his good wife Emma. "But we've planned to go, and go we shall," she added. Sister Burton was never one to make excuses in the Lord's work. This visit to their dear friends the Buckmans, who lived in Australia, was a part of God's work.

They started off as early as possible dressed in the coolest clothes they had. There was just a trail which took them through a thick woods.

"Crunch, crunch, crunch," went their burning feet through the carpet of underbrush.

"Hum, hum, hum," sang mosquitoes in their ears.

Not a breath of air stirred.

"Oh, for a drink of water," they said, but there was no cool spring in sight.

"Crunch, crunch, crunch!"

"Hum, hum, hum!"

On and on they went until finally they came to an opening in the woods where a huge eucalyptus tree had fallen across the river.

"There's our bridge!" exclaimed Brother Burton, for they had to cross the river.

"And look," pointed Emma. "Seats to rest upon formed by the roots."

Brother Burton dropped down on one, a bundle containing some fresh clothing dangling from his arm. His wife stood for a bit, her parasol above her head, enjoying the beautiful cool river with its clean, pebbly bottom.

"How I would like to go into it!" she exclaimed.

That was a dangerous wish. As she turned to Joseph to say, "Well, I may as well sit, too," she tilted back on another seat near by and *crash!* Then *splash!* Sister Burton had her wish. She landed on her feet, parasol still in her hand, with water up to her waist. The sudden jar had caused Brother Burton to lose his balance and he, too, found himself in the river.

"Why, we are all wet!" exclaimed Emma. When they knew they were both safe, they began to laugh. They did look so funny. Wouldn't they make a fine pair to go visiting! They laughed some more. Emma was about to say, "What a good thing that we brought dry clothes along," when she saw the bundle still fastened to her husband's arm, and water streaming from it.

"Why didn't you leave those clean clothes on the bridge?" She grinned.

"I did not know I was coming here or I should have left myself there," was his reply, and they laughed some more.

126

This unexpected bath had cooled them off nicely, but they were ready to get out. That wasn't so simple, however. The water was too deep in the middle of the stream for Emma to wade to the other side. The bank was too high on their side to think of climbing. With much clinging and clawing, and help from Joseph, Emma finally reached shore, and Brother Burton waded across. Emma dried her skirt while he wrung out his socks and picked leeches from his ankles. Then the Burtons went on their way.

Sister Buckman was standing in the doorway when they arrived.

"There! You've fallen into the river, just as I feared!" she cried.

They were soon in dry clothes and seated at a delicious meal.

Later other friends came. As they listened to the Burtons' story, they saw how serious it really had been and explained the danger of the sharp rocks on the bottom in some places.

"Be careful of your wishes," they said, smiling. At the same time all were silently thanking God for his protection.

44

THE FAITHFUL MISSIONARY HORSE

(A true story)

Emma and Joseph Burton were missionaries. They had a good horse whose name was Brum. They had chosen him because his owner had said, "He is a faithful horse."

The Burtons bought a buggy, too, and one morning they started off on a journey of one hundred and eighty miles.

"Our money is almost gone," said Joseph.

"Do not fear," said Emma. "Brum will take us to Yarmouth, and God will go with us."

They paid their way as long as their money lasted. Always they remembered Brum. His lunch of oats cost ten cents at noon, and twenty-five cents bought him food and a place to rest each night. But finally the Burton's money was gone. The last dime had been spent for Brum's lunch. It was long past suppertime, and all three of them were hungry. Emma prayed as they rode along, "Please, dear Father, give us this day our daily bread."

Before long Brum slowed up before a friendly looking house.

"Let us stop here and ask for a room," said Emma.

"Why, surely you may have a room," smiled the friendly people who lived in the friendly house. Brum was fed and put to rest. Then the four sat and visited.

"We are missionaries," explained Joseph, as he told them about Jesus' church of the latter days. It was soon bedtime.

"Would you like some strawberries?" asked the woman.

Nothing ever tasted so good! Covered with rich, yellow cream, they were just what the Burtons needed.

"Our faithful missionary horse knew where to stop." Joseph laughed as they were getting ready for bed.

"And God answered our prayer," said Emma happily. "Those strawberries were our daily bread."

45

THE
OPEN
GATE

One day long years ago, when Joseph and Emma Burton were on a missionary journey with their faithful horse Brum, they came to a small town. It was almost lunchtime, and they were tired and hungry.

"We have no money, but perhaps we shall see an open gate and Brum will turn," said Joseph.

Emma had a headache. "If I could only lie down for a while." She sighed.

On and on they drove. None of the homes looked very inviting. Around their yards were high fences, and every gate was closed.

"They seem to say, 'Stay out!'" said Emma.

Soon they had ridden through the town.

"Surely a farm home will welcome us," Joseph said comfortingly.

The day was very warm, and Emma's head ached more and more. Even Brum was showing signs of weariness. They went on until it was two o'clock. Then they saw a place where the gate was open, and there was hay on the ground. Brum stopped and turned in. That hay looked too good to pass up.

The Burtons were welcomed into the humble home. The young woman of the house opened the door into her best room where the only furniture was some small wooden chairs. Emma looked out into the kitchen. She saw a low couch. It looked so tempting.

"May I please rest on your couch for a while?" she asked. "I have such a bad headache."

"Oh, yes." The woman smiled. "I'll spread a clean cloth and get you a fresh pillow. The men rest there, and it is rather mussed."

"How good this feels. Thank you so much."

After a bit the woman spoke. "Would you like something to eat?"

Emma answered, "Food would taste good. I have not eaten since morning."

"Nor your husband, either?" exclaimed the woman.

Joseph was still outside taking care of Brum.

"No," Emma answered. "Neither of us. Missionaries do not always have money."

"Well, I haven't much but I shall be happy to prepare what I have." She went to work, and in a few minutes Joseph and Emma sat down to a lunch of good homebaked bread with sweet, tasty butter and boiled eggs.

"Nothing ever tasted so good," they agreed.

"And my headache has left," said Emma. "Perhaps this was what I needed."

They visited with the young woman as they ate and after a bit they started to leave.

"Just a minute," said the woman. "My mother, who

is an invalid, lives here with me. She is in her bedroom. I wonder if you would visit with her a while, too."

"Why, of course." They followed her into the room where they found the old woman lying on her bed. Her face brightened as the missionary and his wife talked with her, telling her stories of their experiences. They told her how God had always watched out for them.

"Why even today he led us to your place by way of the open gate," said Emma.

46

THE HOUSE
ON THE
HILL

(A true story)

Brum, the Burtons' faithful missionary horse, stamped his feet impatiently. It was a cold and windy day. Fine snow filled the air, and Brum had been standing in one place for a very long while.

"Pretty soon now, Brum, your master will be here," said Emma. "I'm about frozen, too." She pulled the brightly colored lap robe more closely about her. Her teeth were chattering, and she was shivering from head to foot.

Emma's husband Joseph was a missionary, and friends had told him the people at this house would give him shelter.

"You'll find them very nice people," Joseph had been told. And they *were* good people but they did not feel friendly toward Joseph's church. So many untrue stories had been told about it, and they were believed by these people.

Emma watched her husband as he hurried toward her.

"What's the matter, Joseph?" she asked.

"Let us drive on," he answered, climbing into the buggy. "See that farmhouse away up on the hill, Brum?

133

Well, that's where we're going. Giddap, my boy."

The horse started off at a good trot.

"Will they give us shelter from this storm?" asked Emma.

"I think they will," Joseph nodded as he spoke.

"Goodness!" exclaimed Emma. "I just can't understand how anyone would turn people away in a storm like this."

"We'll let our heavenly Father be their judge."

"You're right, Joseph," she decided.

Soon they reached the gate at the foot of the hill and took the lane which led them to the backyard close to the house. The man of the house was waiting at the back door. Before Brum had hardly come to a standstill, he came quickly forward to unharness. "Take your wife into the house out of this storm," he said, "and I will attend to your horse."

"Perhaps you had better not unharness until you learn who we are," said Joseph.

"It does not make any difference," he replied. "You are cold and perhaps hungry. I saw you turned away from that house down below the hill, but you won't be turned away here!"

Joseph and Emma were guests in this home for three days. Joseph held meetings, and even the man who had refused them shelter became friendly. Emma and the farmer's wife spent happy afternoons in a small, back living room, cozy with its warm fire and bright braided rugs. They knitted and sewed together as Emma told the woman of their many experiences.

"May God always bless this home on the hill," said Joseph, as he and Emma made plans to continue their missionary journey.

47

NEEDED—
FOUR
DOLLARS

(A true story)

"Oh, what a storm!" exclaimed Joseph, the good missionary. He and his wife, Emma, were standing before the window in their room. They had been snowbound for several days.

"Brum says we aren't going to get far without a sleigh," continued Joseph.

Emma smiled. "Oh, he does? Well, doesn't Brum know that we have only two dollars to our name? Does he know where we can buy a sleigh for two dollars?"

"No, but I've heard of one for six dollars. I guess the Lord will have to help out, for I don't see that we can help ourselves."

The Burtons were enjoying their visit in the home of a family named Haley. Mrs. Haley had been so good to them, but they knew they must continue their journey.

"You're like a mother to me," Emma had told her more than once.

Walter, the son, had been kind to Joseph, too. Brother

Burton had been holding meetings in the Haley home, and already one of Walter's brothers had been baptized.

"But we can't stay here all winter, no matter how good they are to us," said Emma.

"The Haleys will store our buggy in the barn," Joseph said with a grin. "Ah, if we just had that sleigh."

"If we just had four dollars, you mean," reminded Emma.

That evening, as the missionary and his wife knelt in prayer together, they asked God to help them out. No one but God knew of their great need. They felt he understood.

When the snow had quit falling and the roads were better, Walter Haley said one morning, "I'm going to town. There ought to be some mail."

"Oh, how nice," said Emma. "I hope we will all get some letters."

A few hours later, Walter returned, exclaiming, "It's really cold!" He clapped his hands before the cheery fire.

"And did you bring us some mail?" asked Emma.

Walter handed her a big fat letter.

"Oh, thank you," said Emma, as she went to find her husband.

"A letter from Brother Holt, Joseph," she called handing it to him.

Emma sat down across from her husband as he opened the letter. In a minute he asked, "Do you see what I have in my hand?"

And then Emma's eyes filled with tears, for there in his hand was the answer to their prayers.

Never before had they received money in the mail. They knew God had caused Brother Holt to send the four dollars.

EMMA PAYS TITHING

(A true story)

Joseph Burton, one of Jesus' helpers of long ago, and his good wife, Emma, lived for many months as missionaries. Scarcely a day passed that they were not in their sleigh, going from place to place talking, singing, preaching. Sometimes there were those who asked to be baptized into Jesus' church of the latter days. What happy times the Burtons had! First a day and night in one home, then another day and night in another home.

"Now, Brum, we are going to Brother Dimock's," said Joseph one day. "Scamper along." Brum took off at a fast trot. Brother Dimock's barn was warm and there was plenty of oats.

As they rode along that day, there was a frown upon Emma's face.

"And what troubles my dear wife?" asked Joseph.

"It's our tithing, Joseph." Money was very scarce. They were receiving no money from the church at this time. Emma sometimes sold some sewing lessons, but she had earned little lately.

"I've thought that maybe I didn't owe any tithing, you see, but today as I've been thinking it over, I'm not so sure."

That night after they were settled in their cozy room at the Dimock home, Emma sat down and figured up what she felt she should have paid in tithing.

"It's five dollars! If ever I get another five dollars, I'm going to pay it, even though I never get another dollar."

The next day the Burtons were passing the home of a friend. The woman called, "Yoo, hoo! Wait a minute."

She came out to the sleigh. "I didn't ever dream I could pay you the money I owe you for the lessons this soon," she said and smiled. "But it has worked out so that I can." She handed Emma five dollars!

"Why, thank you," gasped Emma, too amazed to say more.

"How I wish it had been a few dollars more," Emma told Joseph later. They needed so many things. Her shoes were broken down and so were Brum's.

"And we're out of stamps and envelopes. Oh, dear!"

Joseph did not say a word. Emma was the bookkeeper, and she would decide in the right way.

A few days later the Bishop had a letter from Emma and the five dollars for tithing. She had borrowed an envelope and a stamp.

Then a most wonderful thing happened. A letter came from a good brother of the church. With it was a twenty-dollar gold piece!

"I feel you need this," he wrote. Truly the heavenly Father was blessing Joseph and Emma Burton in many, many ways, and never again did Emma fail to pay their tithing.

49

EXCITEMENT AT CAMP

(A true story)

"We're camping out tonight! Hooray! Hooray!" shouted seven happy children. Their voices carried into the empty house which Mother and Father Burton were leaving.

"Just listen to them," smiled Mother Burton. "Well, let's go. I hope we have everything."

"Don't know where we'd put another thing," her husband said, laughing as they went outside. There before them stood three covered wagons loaded down with tents, bedding, and cooking utensils. Frank, their boy, and his friend, Willie Walker, were on horseback. The other children were finding places in the wagons. All were eager to start; even the horses were stamping their feet impatiently. The Burtons and their friends, the Walkers, were leaving for a new home in another part of California. This, of course, was many, many years ago.

At last they were off. Noon came before they realized it. They stopped under the shade of a large oak tree for their lunch and to stretch their legs. They usually traveled late each day.

One evening something very exciting happened. They had chosen a beautiful campsite with a clear brook running close by. The children were delighted.

The men and boys took care of the horses while the others looked about for places to put up the tents.

"I'll get the rake," exclaimed Dora. All the girls took turns scraping the sticks and pebbles off the ground where the tents were to stand. Later the men put up the tents and unloaded. Fuel was gathered for the fire, and the women cooked the supper. Yum! Yum! How good it tasted!

Soon the dishes were washed and the beds made for the night. The children ran for some of the horses' hay to put under the mattresses which were laid upon the ground. After some romping they all gathered around the fire. It was fun to watch the burning logs. The night was cool, and the fire felt good. They sang the songs of Zion and talked of God's many kindnesses to them. Then all knelt for prayers. As they arose there stood a man. His face had an unkind look.

"What do you want?" he was asked.

"Want to light my cigar," he muttered. "I'm on my way to find a doctor. My father's sick." He looked around curiously. Mother Burton was suddenly very much afraid that he was a robber. She slipped away from the fire and into the tent, hoping she had not been seen. Very quietly she moved one of the vegetable boxes, dug away the sand, and hid a purse of money. When she returned she saw the man riding off.

"The danger is not over yet," they decided. "He may have been a spy. If he was he will come back in the night."

140

As they made ready for bed, they placed their rifles close by. The children were excited and tried to keep awake but soon they were sleeping peacefully. Father Burton was snoring. But Mother Burton could not sleep. The moon threw tree shadows across the tent and they looked like people moving outside. She lifted the flap and peered out. All was quiet. "Where is my faith in God?" she asked herself. Finally she shook her husband.

"Will you please ask the Lord to help me not to be afraid?"

"You need have no more fears," he told her. "An angel stood by me in my dream and said, 'Fear not; no harm shall come to any of you.'"

What a comfort! Mother Burton wondered why she had ever doubted, for now she knew that God had them in his care. And this wonderful promise of protection stayed with her all the way to their new home.

50

NEW
SHOES
FOR FRANK

(A true story)

Do you like to read true stories? This one is true. It happened many years ago. Frank Burton lived with his mother and father and sisters in the state of California. His father was a minister whose work took him away much of the time. Frank did a great deal of the work at home.

One day, as the boy started to the field to plow, his mother said, "Son, your shoes are nearly gone. We *must* get you some new ones."

"But what can we use for money?" asked the boy, as he left the house. I wonder, too, thought his mother. True, there was no money, but something had to be done. That night, after seeing her boy come in with sore feet, she spoke to her husband, who had returned home.

"Joseph, something must be done about shoes for Frank. His old ones are so broken down that today he kicked them off and went barefooted!"

"Oh, no!" interrupted her husband.

"Yes, Joseph. I know you haven't realized his need because you have been away from home so much. I haven't wanted to worry you. But the ground is damp and cold. His feet are so sore he can hardly walk. Besides, there are rattlesnakes everywhere. He plowed up several and came near stepping on one."

They sat quietly for a few minutes. Then Mr. Burton said, "Emma, let us sell our tent. There's a man not far away who needs one. That will give us some money."

Happily they made their plans. The next morning Frank's father put the tent in the wagon and started off. His wife went about her work singing. At last her boy was to have shoes. Her husband returned much sooner than she had expected. Seeing no tent in the wagon, she was sure he had sold it. She was smiling when she met him at the door.

Frank's father was smiling, too.

"Well, I see you have sold the tent!" exclaimed Mrs. Burton. "Did you get the money?"

"No," he replied. "I did not sell it. I didn't even see the man." He was still smiling.

"Then where is it?" his wife questioned, and her heart felt as heavy as lead.

"I hope you will not feel bad about it, Emma," began her husband, "but you see, I let Brother Coons have it."

Brother Coons was an old man who had moved into the neighborhood. He had no home or relatives in California. As Mr. Burton had started on his way that morning, he had met the old fellow who was coming to ask if he might borrow the tent to live in.

"What else could I do?" said Frank's father. "I told him I had it in the wagon and would put it up for him."

Before Mr. Burton had finished speaking, the tears were chasing each other down Mrs. Burton's face. She could not blame her husband. It would have seemed most unneighborly to have refused. Still, she kept thinking of Frank's bare feet on that cold, windy day. She could not help feeling sad.

"There'll be a way yet," said her husband kindly.

Later, after dinner was finished and the dishes were washed, the mother sat down to her sewing before the window. In and out went her needle, in and out, in and out. Her little girls were at school, and the home was very quiet. Yes, in and out went her needle, but she was not thinking of her sewing.

"How can we get our boy some shoes?" she said to herself. Suddenly her answer came. "I will go at once!" she exclaimed.

Laying aside her work, she went to her room. Kneeling at the bedside, she told God all about it.

"Father, please help us to get five dollars, for thou knowest our need." It seemed odd to ask God for dollars but, as she left the room, she said to herself, "It's dollars I need, so I suppose it is right to say dollars." She went back to her sewing with a happy heart, knowing God had heard her prayer.

It seemed almost as if an angel had been sent right down from heaven to take care of her prayer. In the field next to theirs a man was plowing. His name was Brother Mills. He was making his home with the Burton family until he could move into his own home. As he passed near the Burtons' house, a feeling came to him that he should go in and give Frank's mother a five-dollar bill.

"That's foolish," he said to himself. "They aren't in need of money." He kept on plowing until he had gone

144

around the field again. Then a very wonderful thing happened. As he came to the spot where he had first had the feeling, it came again.

"Go, give her five dollars. She needs it." It was as if a voice had spoken. Brother Mills kicked the clods of dirt at his feet. He took off his hat and put it on again, saying to himself, "It will hurt her feelings. She will think I do not feel I am welcome." He started up the team of horses and again went around the field.

As he neared the spot where he had sensed someone speaking to him, the third time he felt he must go into the house. Somehow he knew an unseen angel stood there. He hurried in.

Yes, Frank got his new shoes. As his mother stood in the living room, holding the five-dollar bill which Brother Mills had given her, the boy came into the house.

"Oh, Mother! Where did you get that?" he exclaimed.

Mrs. Burton told the whole story.

"Oh, how wonderful! Now you can get my shoes!" said the boy excitedly.

With joyful hearts and praises to God, they gave thanks for his goodness to them.

51

DORA
AND THE
ROLLER

(A true story)

One beautiful California morning many years ago, Addie and Dora Burton and their friend Millie Perdue skipped along on the way to school.

Suddenly Dora exclaimed, "Oh, look at the big roller hooked on to that wagon. What is it for?"

"To break up the hard ground." Millie laughed. "The driver's going right past the school. Let's get up on the tongue of the wagon."

"I'm scared," spoke Addie, who was younger.

"I'm not," boasted Dora. "It's plenty wide enough. Come on."

Addie watched as the girls climbed on. Just then, the man in the wagon, who had stopped to talk with some of the men working nearby and had not seen the children, called out to his horses, "Giddap!" and started up the road.

The sudden jolt of starting caused Millie to sway

146

forward as if she were about to fall. Dora reached out and pulled her friend back. But Dora lost her balance and fell lengthwise of the road. The huge roller kept going until it had gone over Dora's feet and on over her head.

Addie and Millie cried, "Help! Help!" The driver of the wagon stopped.

A crowd gathered quickly. Old Brother Brush, one of the men who had been working nearby, hurried over. He felt sure that Dora was dead. But as he lifted her up, she opened her eyes and said, "Oh, Father Brush, administer to me." The old man raised his eyes to heaven in prayer. Then he carried her to the nearest house and laid her upon a bed. Other elders had come, and Dora was administered to.

Little Addie had run back home calling, "Mother! Mother! Dora was run over by the big roller! Come quick!"

Mrs. Burton felt all her strength leave as she thought of that great, monstrous thing rolling over her child's body. It was eight or ten feet long, she knew, and must weigh more than a thousand pounds.

As they hurried along the frightened mother asked, "Is she dead?"

"No," sobbed Addie. "She was alive when I left."

A prayer came to the mother's heart as she ran. She was comforted by a voice which she alone heard. "Be of good cheer," it said.

She found Dora's body badly swollen, especially her head and ears.

"My poor child," soothed the mother. Her greatest wish right then was to get Dora home.

"But she can't be moved," spoke up several.

One neighbor, seeing how anxious Mrs. Burton was, said, "I will help you." He left the house, soon to return with a light wagon. Both seats had been taken out and straw placed in the bottom. Four men gently raised the bed by the corners and lifted Dora, bed and all, in. Slowly the horses were led to the Burton home.

Dora cried with pain as her clothes were removed. Soon she was ready for her own little bed. Someone had called a doctor, who examined her carefully and said, "It will be several months before that girl walks."

Dora's father came home from a preaching mission to help. Neighbors were all helpful.

Every hour little Dora seemed to get better. Just two weeks later she went shopping with her mother. How joyously Dora walked at her mother's side. And whom should they meet but the doctor! He stood there in amazement. "It is not possible!" he exclaimed.

Mrs. Burton smiled. "Yes, this is the one who was hurt. She is doing pretty well, is she not?"

"I should think she is!" he retorted and walked away.

Many people heard about the little Burton girl who had been hurt. Some drove to the place of the accident, thinking they might find a hole or rut which would have kept her from being so badly hurt. But they didn't. The road was hard and smooth and level.

"It's a miracle for sure!" they all said.

The Burton family knew the answer. It was God's blessing.

52

ANDY'S ADVENTURE

George Anderson, Jr., better known as Andy, slammed the screen door of the summer cottage and went whistling toward the lake. He wore a bright red swimsuit and carried a box of bait and other necessary fishing apparatus.

"If you practice your violin without any foolishness for a full hour," his mother had said that morning, "I'll give my permission for you to go fishing with the boys this afternoon. It is your own fault, son, that you have been losing out the last few days."

Andy knew his mother was right. He really liked playing the violin, too. It had been his ambition ever since he could remember to someday play as well as his father who was a member of the symphony orchestra and had even given his own concerts. But lately some of the boys whose parents also had summer homes on Lake Echo had been giving him a pretty hard time. He knew they didn't understand about using the talents God gave and all that sort of thing, but just the same he sometimes grew tired of their teasing. He imagined he could hear their taunts now as he ran down the steps of the terrace toward the sandy beach.

"I'll just have to take their kidding," he told himself. He hoped the boys had waited for him.

Andy looked up and down the beach. There was no one in sight.

"I suppose the small fry are all taking their naps," he reasoned, "but where are Jim and Peter and Red?" Jim and Peter were the Wilson twins. They were eleven years old, the same age as Andy. Red Carson, whose real name was Derry, was two years older.

"Maybe they haven't come yet," he said hopefully. And then he noticed the canoes. The green one was missing.

"The Carson canoe is gone," he exclaimed. "They *have* gone without me. Drat them!" He stood there with his fist doubled up. Then he said, "I don't care. I can go by myself."

Andy had never taken the canoe alone and he was pretty sure he should not have done so. He could just hear his mother's emphatic "No!" were he to go back to the cottage and ask her. So he dropped his paraphernalia into the yellow canoe, looked cautiously about, jumped in, and paddled hurriedly off upstream. He felt excited and ashamed at the same time.

Andy knew exactly where he was going. It was a place he and his father had discovered one day when they were out together. They had caught a lot of fish.

"I'll show those old meanies," he gloated. "When the boys see me with a long string of fish they'll wish they hadn't run off from me."

Andy was tired and hot when he reached the secret fishing spot. He felt sticky all over and he was thirsty, too, so the first thing he did was to take a cool drink of water from his thermos bottle. Then he baited his hook and threw the line over the side of the canoe and waited. It was several minutes before there was a bite. Then suddenly he felt the tugging on the line, and with all the strength he could muster he pulled in a beautiful striped bass. It was enormous! Andy was so excited he could hardly get it off the hook. He finally succeeded and soon had the line out again. In almost less time than it takes to tell it he caught another, even larger than the first.

"Boy-oh-boy, luck is sure with me!" he boasted. "Won't the boys be envious of me! And won't Dad be proud when he comes tonight for the Fourth of July vacation?" He could hardly wait to show off his bass. "Maybe Mom won't scold me when she sees these fish." He baited another hook and cast the line.

Andy hadn't noticed the storm clouds that had gathered nor had he been aware of how dark it was getting. A high wind had come up, too, and suddenly huge splatters of rain came down and hit him in the face. The canoe tossed to and fro. He was frightened. He forgot all about the line which he had thrown in and began wishing desperately that he were safe at home. All at once there was a big gust of wind and the next thing he knew he was clinging to the capsized canoe, completely covered with water.

Fortunately Andy was a good swimmer and was able to float about and tread water, but he knew he was really in trouble. He clung to the upturned canoe, trying to right it, but without success.

"Maybe the boys are somewhere near." He grasped the side of the canoe more firmly and called, "Jim! Peter! Red!" There was nothing but the echo of his own voice and the caw, caw, caw of rain crows. He shivered. Then

Andy thought of how he had been bragging. "Where are my fish?" he wondered. "I suppose I was bragging too much about them and thinking unkind thoughts about the boys. I was disobedient, too." It was odd but Andy began to think of his grandfather. "What's that old saying Grandfather was always quoting? 'Pride goeth before a fall,' that's it. I guess he's right and what a splash!" Andy did not know what to do. Then he thought of something else he had heard his grandfather say many times.

"It's manly, my boy, to learn while you're young that the companionship of your heavenly Father is a pretty fine thing to have. You never know when you're going to need God and, what is just as important, when he is going to need you."

"Well, I sure do need you right now, God," Andy prayed. "And I'm sorry for the way I've acted lately about my practicing and for taking the canoe. If I ever get out of this I'm going to practice better and I'll play that piece for the special Fourth of July service and any other time I'm asked . . . without grumbling, too. I'm awful ashamed, God, for everything. I'm not saying these things just so you'll help me out, though of course I would be awful thankful if you would."

This was the first time Andy had ever seen how much a fellow needed God. He had always had almost everything he wanted . . . a good home, his mother and dad, a keen big sister, all the clothes and food he needed, a bike and lots of toys. "Why, I have everything and I've never been nearly thankful enough. How I wish I could see Mom and Dad so I could tell them how I feel."

With greater determination Andy again tried to turn over the canoe. To his surprise what had seemed an impossibility before was easy this time. He let out a "Hooray!" He shouted the second time as he discovered the string upon which his fish were tied still fastened securely to the canoe. Andy said softly, "Thank you, God, for everything." As he climbed into the canoe all the water on his face did not come from the lake. "And I don't care if I am crying," he declared. "I've seen Dad and Grandfather cry when they were happy and thankful. I guess there are times when men can cry and not be sissies, either."

Andy had the feeling that God was very, very close and had truly helped him in his time of need. Again his grandfather's words came to him: "You never know when you're going to need your heavenly Father nor when he's going to need you."

He thought of his violin. "Call on me anytime, God," he said. "I'm going to practice hard so that I'll be ready to help you as you've helped me."

53

THE PEARL NECKLACE

"I'm going to ask Mother if I may wear her pearl necklace to the banquet tonight." Claudia's heart beat faster as she thought of the new pale-green organdy dress hanging in her closet. "Mother's necklace is just what I need," she decided, hurrying up the walk on her way home from school.

She burst into the cool hall. "Mother, I'm home," she called. There was no answer. Then she noticed a note beside the telephone. Claudia sat down on the bottom stairstep and read, "My dear daughter, your grandmother is suddenly very ill and I have gone to her. I hate to leave when the banquet is being held tonight, but I know you will understand. It's too bad your father and Bill will be busy at the store and won't be home to see you leave. Bill says he's going to be late. That's what happens when you have both a dad and brother all wrapped up in the grocery business. There will be no 'ohs' and 'ahs' for you, and it just isn't fair. You do understand, though, don't you? Don't worry about Grandmother. She is going to get along fine, but she wants me and I know I can depend on you.

Ardis' mother says they will stop for you to take you to the banquet. Have a happy time. I'll call you. I love you. Mother."

When Claudia finished reading the note she had almost to pinch herself to realize it was really true. Her mother gone! She just couldn't believe that she was a hundred miles away.

"And tonight of all nights!" she sobbed. She reread the note. "Oh, dear, how selfish I am!" she exclaimed. "Here Grandmother is sick, and I'm thinking only of myself. And if she had known about the banquet she wouldn't have let Mother come. Grandmother is so sweet and thoughtful of others. I need to grow up." She jumped resolutely to her feet and started up the stairs.

"First I'll pray for Grandmother," she said, as she dropped her schoolbooks on the desk in her room and knelt beside her bed. Claudia felt much better after her talk with God. She knew the house was not the same without her mother but at the same time she felt she could manage if she had to; her mother had had enough confidence in her to leave her.

"I'll prove to her that she can depend on me," Claudia decided as she set about getting ready.

Claudia pinned her hair and put on her cap to take a shower. Then she gave herself a manicure. As the clear polish dried she read from her New Testament. She had the habit of reading from one of her church books each day. At present she was in the gospel of John. She loved the beautiful teachings of Jesus. It was surprising how much she had been able to read and how much it had helped her to teach her class of little six-year-olds. Claudia read for fifteen minutes, long after the polish was dry. And then she started to dress. Several times the girl glanced

admiringly at the lovely sheer dress hanging on the door of
the closet.

"Mother has taught me that I must not worship
clothes," she mused, "and I've read many times what
happened to the people of Book of Mormon days when they
forgot God in their worship of clothes and riches. But
surely he wants us to look attractive, and I did save my
allowance for months to buy the material and even made
most of the dress. That is pleasing to him, I know."

She drew the dress over her head and zipped it on
the side, standing before the full-length mirror. Then it
was she remembered the pearls. For several minutes
Claudia stood there in deep thought.

"What shall I do? I wanted to ask Mother if I might
wear them." Slowly she started toward her mother's room.
"She surely won't care. Still, if anything should happen to
them I could never stand it."

She stood uncertainly outside the door of her mother's
room. Finally she slowly pushed it open and went toward
the dressing table. Claudia loved this room. It was here
that she had shared so many confidences with her mother.
It was almost like the sanctuary at church, because of God's
Spirit which she always felt.

"The pearls are in the right-hand drawer in the blue
velvet case," she almost whispered.

"Why do I feel so queer, as if I were stealing?" she
asked herself. Hesitantly she opened the drawer and drew
out the case. She opened it and lifted the pearls to her
neck.

"Oh, they are lovely!" she exclaimed. "Just what I
need." She hummed softly to herself, imagining the way
she would look standing beside the other girls in the sextette
who were to sing at the banquet. "Mother, why did you

have to go away today of all days?" Tears of self-pity came to her eyes.

Claudia came to with a start. "Now aren't you a big baby! Feeling sorry for yourself again. You're selfish, Claudia Jeffries, just downright selfish!" She looked at her reflection in the mirror impatiently. She had suddenly made up her mind. "I won't wear them! It would be all right with Mother if she were here, but it wouldn't be honest to take them without asking."

With the necklace safe in the drawer again, Claudia started back to her own room just as the telephone rang. She ran down the stairs.

"Hello, dear," came her mother's voice.

"Oh, Mom," cried Claudia with delight. "How's Grandmother?"

"Better, dear. I'll stay for a day or two, though, if you can manage."

"Of course we can," Claudia assured her. Suddenly she felt very grown-up and mature. "We'll miss you dreadfully. You know that. I didn't see how I could possibly dress without you, but I look pretty nice if I do say so myself." She heard her mother's chuckle. And then she thought her ears must surely be playing tricks on her. But, no! Mother was asking her something!

"Would you like to wear my pearl necklace, honey? It would set off the dress to perfection, don't you think?"

"Mother, how did you know?" breathed Claudia. "Thank you, thank you, thank you!"

Mrs. Jeffries laughed again.

As she bade her mother good-bye and ran back up to her room to take down her hair Claudia knew she had every reason to thank God, too. "Now I can wear the pearls with a clear conscience," she said happily.

54

THE
RACE

Ben hurriedly tied the strings of his track shoes and ran through the door of the gym to join the other boys who were lining up for track.

This was the tryout for the final half-mile race for the spring tournament. If he were among the winners today he was "in."

"But if I'm not . . ." Ben told himself, "I'll . . . I'll . . ."

Ben hated to think of what his brother, Tim, would say if he failed. All through school his older brother had urged him to try to be as good at everything in sports as he was.

"Sometimes I wish I didn't have an older brother," he admitted to Russ, his best friend, who was energetically exercising his legs up and down in preparation for the race.

Russ grinned as he answered. "Your trouble is that you'd rather have your nose in a book."

Ben retorted, "Well, what's wrong with that? How's winning this race going to help me be a better missionary? Answer me that, will you?"

Russ's grin grew wider. "Maybe missionaries need strong legs so they can run fast when people who don't want to hear about their church take after them," he suggested.

Ever since Ben and Russ had attended a youth camp the previous summer they had talked frequently of church and of their desire to serve as missionaries. Very few knew of this or of the times they had secretly drawn apart from the group into a grove of elm trees where they had prayed together. Not for a million dollars would Ben have let his brother know. All that Tim thought of was sports.

The boys' conversation was brought to a close as their coach, Mr. Garth, came toward them.

"Now, fellows," he said by way of greeting, "remember this is *it*. Some of you are good and some of you are 'gooder.'" They all grinned. He knew that they knew it was not good grammar to say "gooder" and that he used it in fun. "Yes," he repeated, "some are good, others 'gooder,' and a few are 'goodest.' Where you find yourself at the end of the race is not as important as that you have given your very best. Placing for finals is not the important thing. Giving your best *is*—not for your own glory nor the school's, not for your brother's glory [and he looked right at Ben, for he knew how Tim was] but for the feeling within your own heart that you have honestly tried." He looked at his watch.

The boys stood nervously waiting. Ben chewed at his fingernails. Mr. Garth looked him straight in the eye. Could he read his mind? Did he see that had it not been for his brother's teasing he would not even try? All at once Ben felt ashamed. Maybe he was a quitter. Maybe it was because he felt he couldn't win that he pretended he didn't want to. "I'm all mixed up," he told himself just as he was alerted to something the coach was saying.

"Fellows, this race today will determine, in part, your attitude toward many things. Some of you have already decided upon your future careers. For instance, I know

159

Bill here wants to be a surgeon." He pointed to a tall skinny boy standing close to him. "Well, let's look ahead. Let's pretend Bill has 'doctor' before his name. He is in the operating room and the life of his patient depends to a great extent upon his skill and determination to win a different kind of race. Bill is resolved, just as he is today, to give the very best he has in him. Do you see how important it is always to strive for excellence? It helps all through life. One's best is important. A job worth doing is worth doing well." He again looked at his watch. "Three minutes and . . . well, all I ask is that you give your very best."

Every young body straightened up a little taller. Ben and Russ looked seriously at each other. "I guess that goes for missionaries, too, Ben," said Russ in a low voice.

"I guess so," Ben nodded. "Say, do you remember what the youth leader said at camp about Jesus being our coach?"

"Yeh, I'd sort of forgotten it, hadn't you?"

"Uh-huh. And he said that men like Mr. Garth were not only anxious for us to win sports for the school's glory but that they wanted us to learn how to give our best constantly. He said that if we wanted to be on Jesus' team we'd need to learn this."

Just at that moment the first whistle blew. The boys lined up. Ben saw his brother in a crowd of older boys on the other side of the fence. He wished he could tell him that he was going to give everything he had, because somehow he suddenly knew that if he did he'd be a better missionary.

"I guess I've already won one important race," he told himself happily. "I've won a race with my wrong thinking. Here I go!"

160

TAKE
MY
LIFE

Pretty Elizabeth Ann's fingers ran listlessly over the piano keys. She had been practicing all the time her cousins, Nancy and Jane, were playing tennis outside the living room window. She could hear their happy voices now as the ball sailed back and forth through the air. How much she had wanted to join them! Her mother's gentle yet firm admonition still rang in her ears and she felt rebellious even now as she thought of it.

"All your life you are going to have to make choices, my dear," she had said, "and a girl who is fourteen should be old enough to know that life is not all play."

"But, Mother," she had argued, "the girls are only going to be out here on the coast a month. It isn't even polite to let them entertain themselves." She knew she was only making a poor excuse. Her cousins from Illinois loved to play tennis together and they probably weren't missing her at all. The truth was she just didn't want to be the assistant pianist in the children's department at church. She was always having to give up something that was fun to practice the hymns.

Elizabeth Ann looked toward the clock on the mantel. Her brown eyes snapped and she pushed back her soft blonde hair angrily. "Twenty more minutes!" she fumed, pounding out the hymn again, not even looking at the words before her. She just couldn't get the notes in the bass clef right. She could hear her mother humming in the kitchen. "She'll have a hard time singing to my music," Elizabeth Ann told herself ruefully.

When the twenty minutes were up she slammed the front door and ran to the tennis court. "Free at last!" she called to her cousins. But Nancy was tired, so the three girls sat down in the shade of an old walnut tree.

"Why didn't you come sooner?" asked Nancy with a pout on her face. "Jane was beating me and I would have turned the racket over to you gladly. Why do you bother with that old piano practice anyway? I sure wouldn't. If I want music I just turn on TV or the radio."

"Nancy, you shouldn't talk that way to Elizabeth Ann," spoke up Jane. "She should be thankful that she has a talent to use for God."

"Piffle!" exclaimed Nancy. "It looks too much like work to me." She stretched out on the grass and closed her eyes.

"Look at her," complained Jane with a sigh. "There's a girl who sings like a lark and she has never yet used her talent for God. I'd give anything if I could sing like that. I want so much to show God how much I love him."

Elizabeth Ann looked at her cousin. Jane's face had a faraway expression. She had known ever since the girls had come to her house that they were different. Jane was fun, as much fun as anyone, but she always had time to help about the house, too. She played with Tony, Elizabeth Ann's little brother, and no one could tell Bible stories as she did. Tony would sit and listen with his eyes never leaving Jane's face.

As Elizabeth Ann braided a clover wreath she questioned Jane. "Why do you wish for Nancy's talent? You have one of your own. There isn't anyone who can tell stories as well as you can."

"Maybe that is a talent," answered Jane with a smile. "I do love to tell them and I always feel God close to me when I do. I often help out at church back home."

Just as Elizabeth Ann started to say more she heard her mother calling. "Time to set the table for lunch. Come, girls. I can use about six extra hands."

"Wake up, sleepyhead," said Jane, tickling her sister's bare toes which stuck out through her green sandals.

Nancy yawned. "Let me alone," she whined.

"Here, I'll put this clover wreath on her head and we'll crown her 'Lady of Leisure,' " said Elizabeth Ann with a laugh. She was remembering the many times her cousin had avoided work, leaving her and Jane to do it while she watched television or posed before the mirror.

"I'm sleepy, you pests," Nancy repeated. "Call me when lunch is ready." She turned her back to them.

"That girl!" said Jane. "She's just too lazy to live."

Later in the day, after having gone swimming and lounging on the beach most of the afternoon, the girls returned home and changed their clothes. Then they went into the kitchen where Elizabeth Ann's mother had sparkling glasses of lemonade waiting for them.

"How about some ping-pong before supper?" asked Elizabeth Ann of the two girls.

"Don't you think you had better go over your music for church tomorrow first, dear?" asked her mother, looking up from a pan of peas she was shelling.

Elizabeth Ann's first impulse was to make a sharp retort. The she saw Jane's eyes smiling into hers. She thought of their earlier conversation under the tree.

"Maybe I am fortunate in having a talent I can use for God," she said to herself. "I really don't believe I'd want to be like Nancy—just playing and eating and sleeping and listening to the radio or watching television all day long—and making myself pretty." She watched Nancy admiring her image before a mirror. Come to think of it, she thought, Jane is much prettier.

Nancy interrupted her train of thought. "Why are you staring at me like that, Elizabeth Ann?" she queried.

Elizabeth Ann flushed. "Ever since you girls first came I've been trying to decide which is the prettier. Now I think I know."

"Oh, you do, do you?" Nancy's underlip hung low. "I suppose it's Jane."

Elizabeth Ann made no reply, but to herself she was thinking that Nancy was positively ugly when she pouted like that and Jane's beauty was something that shone from within like a bright light. She watched Jane sit down beside her mother and start shelling peas. "Here, I'll give you a hand, Auntie," Jane said with a smile. Then she looked again at Nancy who had sprawled out on the floor with a comic book she had taken from her pocket. Elizabeth Ann *knew* she didn't want to be like Nancy.

"Okay," she answered her mother cheerfully, "and I

164

just bet you I'll get those bass notes right or I'll sit at the piano all night."

"Bravo," said Jane.

Elizabeth Ann swished around and went whistling into the living room. Sitting down at the piano she opened the hymbook which she had closed with a bang in the morning. The words of the hymn which she hadn't even bothered to read before now seemed like beautiful jewels in a treasure chest. She sang them softly and reverently:

> "Take my life, and let it be
> Consecrated, Lord, to thee;
> Take my moments and my days;
> Let them flow in ceaseless praise;
>
> "Take my hands, and let them move
> At the impulse of thy love;
> Take my feet, and let them be
> Swift and beautiful for thee."

She sang all six stanzas. Her fingers ran lightly over the keys without even one fumble. "Why," she said earnestly—and it was like a prayer—"I *do* want to give my life, my talents, everything I have. I want to use my hands and let them move over the keys like the hymn says, 'At the impulse of his love.' I never felt this way before. It is an opportunity to have a talent and use it for God's church." She played as she had never played before. She began the hymn again, loving the words as she sang. Then suddenly another voice, clear and bell-like, joined with hers and the music carried through the house. She turned around. There stood Nancy, and there were tears in her eyes.

"Do you suppose they'd let me sing a solo some time while I'm here?" she asked. "I'm ashamed of myself for being so selfish with the voice God gave me. You know, as you sang those words all at once I saw myself for the first time and I've been a pill, a nasty pill."

"Of course they'll let you sing," answered Elizabeth Ann, and she squeezed her cousin's hand. "But how could you change so fast?"

"It was that look you gave me awhile ago," Nancy confessed. "I knew you weren't the only one who compared Jane with me and found me ugly."

"You're not really ugly," Elizabeth Ann assured her. "Why, right now you are beautiful."

"Then it's because I am thinking some beautiful thoughts for a change."

Jane came up behind them quietly. "And maybe I can tell a story in junior church," she said, "and we'll all three be using our talents for God."

"You sure can," spoke up little Tony who at that moment came into the room. "I've already told all the kids what a good storyteller you are."

"Well," said Elizabeth Ann, "it looks as if having talents and using them is the way to make a lot of people happy." She played the hymn once more and as the girls' voices rang out, God's Spirit filled the house.

56

JIMMY'S BLESSING

(A true experience of the Blair family told by
A. D. Blair, Jimmy's brother)

One cold, winter night in Iowa years ago, the door of the Blair's simple, one-room house slammed shut with a bang.

"Br-r-r, it's cold!" exclaimed Father Blair, as he and his two older sons, Cliff and Ray, walked toward the red-hot stove to warm themselves.

"Is it still snowing, Daddy?" questioned four-year-old David. He had had great fun standing in the window, watching the snowflakes tumble down until darkness had settled on the outside world.

"Not now, son, but the wind is sharp and cold. Cliff and Ray and I are just about frozen, but now that the stock have been fed and taken care of for the night, we can enjoy our food and rest. It's good to be inside." He removed his wraps and hung them on a peg nearby, then sat down before the open oven to warm his toes.

"When do we eat, Mom?" asked Cliff, the older boy, as he hung his coat and cap beside his father's. "I'm starved."

"Here, too," added Ray. "Supper smells good."

"Just as quickly as you three hungry bears get washed." Mother Blair smiled. She and Valda, the boys' big sister, were taking up the warm food and placing it upon the table. It was a homey scene. Every bit of space was taken up with furniture and the family, but it was warm and clean. There were two large beds, and a small trundle bed was pushed beneath one of the large ones during the day. A bureau stood at one side of the room and there were several chairs. It was really cramped. Baby Neva lay in her cradle sleeping, and Jimmy, who was just learning to walk and talk, had been put in his high chair where he was laughing at his big brother Ray who was clapping his hands together to warm them. Little Jimmy thought it was a game and clapped his own chubby hands in glee.

"David, come let sister wash you," said Valda. In a short while all were ready and seated at the table with bowed heads as the blessing was asked upon the food.

It was a good supper, with laughter and lively talk about school as the meal was eaten. The older ones had many interesting stories to tell, and David listened with interest.

"Someday I'm going to school," he beamed. "Someday when I'm six."

"Yes, son," smiled his mother, "but now you are my little helper. Why, I need you to help with Jimmy and baby sister." She patted his head lovingly.

"What did our boy do today?" asked Father.

"Lots of things," answered the child. "And tomorrow I'm going to make a big, big snowman, and Mother is going to put Jimmy right up close to the window where he can watch."

"Well, don't put my cap on your snowman's head as you did last time," joked Cliff.

"I won't," promised David, as he took another piece of cornbread and dipped it into the golden honey which covered his plate. "I'm going to make Daddy Butler 'cause next to Daddy he's the nicest man in the whole, wide world." Daddy Butler, the elder of their little congregation of Saints, was adored by both old and young.

When supper was over, Valda washed the dishes and the older boys dried them, carrying on a noisy argument as to which one would get the third comfortable chair. Every night it was a race to this chair. Mother sat in her rocker, Father in his big easy chair, and whoever was luckiest got the third one. The others were not so comfortable.

"I win," shouted Ray, as he dried the last dish hurriedly and tossed the towel carelessly over the rack. He fell into the chair just as Mother looked up from her mending beside the one big lamp in the room.

"Ray," she admonished, "go back and hang that towel properly."

He got up reluctantly and when his back was turned, Cliff who had been right at hand, slipped into the chair.

The tussle that followed provided amusement for the entire family. Finally, however, all was peace and quiet. The older children were reading their schoolbooks, Father had his big Bible before him, and Mother continued with the pile of socks. David was building with his blocks on the floor at her feet.

"Look, Mother," he said. "I'm going to have forty-seven rooms in my house, one for each one of us."

They all laughed. "Eight will be enough," spoke up Ray, who was just learning arithmetic at school and felt very superior.

"Well, even two would be a help," put in Father.

"It would be nice to have more room," agreed Mother, "but as long as we are all well and happy together, I won't complain." Often they talked of the time when they would have a bigger house, and always Mother made them feel thankful for the blessings they already had.

David thought how much he loved her and then he decided to climb up into her lap and cuddle close. There wasn't much time now for this, as little Neva and Jimmy took so much of her time. He loved to snuggle in his mother's arms. He jumped up quickly, stumbled on one of his blocks, and then almost before he knew what was happening he had struck little Jimmy's high chair. It fell on the red-hot stove and Jimmy's face lay against the very hottest part.

Father picked him up and laid him in Mother's arms. He cried and cried. All the children were crying. "Oh, I didn't want to do it, Mother," sobbed David. "I didn't want to do it."

"Of course not, child," comforted Mother. "It was just an awful, awful accident." All the while the little fellow cried loudly. An ointment for burns was used but still he screamed in great pain.

"I'm going for Daddy Butler," declared Father, reaching for his wraps. "Come, Cliff and Ray, get into your things. It won't take the three of us long to get the team hitched."

All the time they were gone Jimmy lay in his mother's arms, crying at the top of his voice. The others stood about not knowing what to do. Baby Neva stirred and began to cry, too, and Valda warmed some milk for her. David stood with his face pressed against the window, every little bit wiping the tears from his eyes.

170

"Oh, please, God," he prayed softly to himself, "help them to hurry and bring Daddy Butler, and please make Jimmy well so he won't cry." He watched and watched.

After what seemed a long, long time he exclaimed eagerly, "Here they come, Mother! Here they come! Now Baby Jimmy will stop crying."

In a very short while Daddy Butler was standing at Mother's side looking down into the face of the burned child. He asked them all to kneel and pray with him. Then very gently he placed the consecrated oil upon Jimmy and laid his hands upon his head, asking God to make him well.

Almost as if God were right there in the room, Jimmy stopped crying, and in a few minutes was fast asleep. Daddy Butler thanked God again for his great blessing. David and the others were thanking Him in their hearts.

After Father and the boys returned from taking Brother Butler home, the family went to bed quietly, and in the morning Jimmy's face was much, much better. It had already begun to heal. As the days came and went it was evident that there would be no scar. How thankful they all were. David never forgot God's goodness to them.

57

WHO'S THERE

An air of excitement hung over the large white house on Maple Street where the Griffiths lived. A big yellow van had drawn up to the little brown cottage across the street. The Griffiths, seated at the breakfast table, were all staring out the window.

"New neighbors!" exclaimed Merna Kay, her brown eyes sparkling. "Oh, do you suppose there will be a girl our age?" she asked, turning to her twin sister, Donna Mae, who looked just like her.

"This neighborhood has enough girls," teased their brother, Bing. "I hope there's a boy. We need him to make up our ball club—and an older one for umpire."

"Boys!" muttered Merna Kay.

"Yes, boys!" repeated Donna Mae.

"We'll take what we get," suggested Daddy. "And we'll like them." He got up from the table.

"We'll just be thankful the house is occupied. I declare, I have been so tired looking at those drawn blinds. I just hope whoever moves in will put up some fluffy tiebacks or something pretty," said Mother.

"Who owns the house, anyway?" asked Bing.

"Why, an old couple by the name of Wilson," replied his father. "They moved away years ago, when their family grew too large. They have rented the house ever since."

"So, you see," said Mother, "it won't be a *large* family. One child, perhaps."

"I hope it's a girl," said Merna Kay.

"I do, too," said Donna Mae.

"I don't. I hope it's a boy," said Bing, not to be outdone.

Father left for work and the children soon left for school. They stopped briefly to watch the furniture being moved into the house, but they saw only two very busy men and walked on dejectedly.

The house became a place of mystery as the days came and went and there was no activity across the street.

"Why would they move their furniture in and then not come themselves?" queried Bing, his gray eyes puzzled. "And all the time we are needing a big boy to help us on our team."

"How do you know there will be a boy?" scoffed Merna Kay.

"Yes, don't be so sure," added Donna Mae. "We girls in the neighborhood are organizing a 'be-kind-to-your-neighbors' club and we want her to join."

"Her?" shouted Bing.

Mother and Father laughed. "Well, all I ask for is a neighbor who will put up some curtains," said Mother.

"I wonder if there will be a man in the family," mused Father.

Several more days passed. Then one day things began to happen. In the first place, Bing, who usually started his day off by feeding his dog Rusty, came back into the house exclaiming, "Rusty has a new friend! The cutest little black Scotty you ever saw! Our new neighbors must have moved in after dark last night."

"Oh, goody, goody, goody!" shouted Donna Mae.

"I bet the dog belongs to a little girl," said Merna Kay.

"It's a boy's dog, I just know it is," declared Bing.

"I'm going over and see," their mother informed them. "I'll take some of these warm cinnamon rolls."

"May I go, too?" asked Bing.

The girls begged, "Let us go."

"No, I'll go alone this time," their mother told them, wrapping the rolls in waxed paper. She took off her kitchen apron, tied a gay red scarf around her head, and slipped out the back door.

"I never saw such curiosity," said Father, grinning. Then he slyly added, "It would be a good joke on Mother if our new neighbors turned out to be one lone bachelor."

They ate nervously, eyes glued to the back door, ears tuned for the first footstep on the porch. After what seemed an endless wait, Mother came bursting in, her eyes shining. "Guess what!" she exclaimed.

"What?" they all said in one breath.

"It's the Wilsons! They've come back to live in the little house where they first started housekeeping! Isn't that sweet?"

"No girls?" cried Merna Kay.

"No girls?" echoed her sister.

Bing looked aghast. "Just an old man and an old woman. Aw, shucks, anyway!"

"Now, look here," spoke up Father, "I think we need a little family talk."

"You're right, Father," agreed Mother. "They're just

as sweet as they can be, and everyone in this family must think of ways to make them feel welcome in their own home."

No one spoke for a moment. Then suddenly both girls began talking at once. "Our 'be-kind-to-your-neighbors' club," said Merna Kay.

"Yes," agreed Donna Mae. "Oh, we can do a lot of things for them." They danced up and down.

Father looked at Bing. "How about our Boy Scout?" he asked.

"I know, I know," said Bing, entering into the spirit the girls had shown, "There'll be a hundred things I can do to help them."

Mother smiled. "And let me tell you something else. Mr. Wilson knows all about baseball. He'll make a wonderful umpire, and Mrs. Wilson loves girls and boys. She said she wanted you girls to come to her house for your club meetings very soon."

"Hurray! Hurray!" shouted the children.

"Thank you, God, for children who are thinking most of ways they can make others happy," prayed Mrs. Griffith as she went about her work later. "Thank you for such a wonderful family."

58

PAT
THE
PARAKEET

"But why can't I have the parakeet?" begged Lucy,
tears in her brown eyes. "The pet-store man says he's
a very smart bird. And Trudy has one. I want one, too."

Her father stood at the door of her room. "Do you
really want to know?" he questioned her. "If so, just
look about your room. Here is your answer. Your mother
already has plenty to do. A parakeet would only add to
her work."

"But I'll take care of it," insisted Lucy.

"The way you do your room?" her father asked as he
slowly turned and walked away.

Lucy looked about her room. It certainly was a mess.
Nothing was in order. The pretty yellow dress her mother
had made with such painstaking care had been thrown
carelessly across a chair. The hanger upon which it had
been hung was on the floor, where her pajamas also lay
in a heap. Other wearing apparel was out of place. Shoes
and socks were thrown about. Her tennis racket and ball

were on her dressing table. Her desk was strewn with books and papers.

"It surely looks a sight," Lucy admitted to herself. Then an expression of determination settled over her face. "I'll show them!" she decided as she went to work. "Then maybe they'll think that I am big enough to have the parakeet." Soon it looked like a different room. And Lucy had a happy feeling because she had done it all herself.

That night when she went to turn down the covers of her bed, she found pinned to her pillow a note written in her father's handwriting but signed "Pat, the Parakeet," It read: "Dear Lucy, I came to see you today and I am beginning to think I'd like to stay. Yesterday your room was in such a mess that I was afraid you wouldn't take any better care of me than you do of your pretty clothes which your father works hard to provide and which mother sews for you. There are other homes where I feel I might be given better care, though I'm sure you can help me decide that your home is a good place for me. How about it? I'll be checking daily."

Lucy was so excited that she could hardly wait to tell her friend, Trudy. And she could hardly keep from talking about it that night at the dinner table. Instead, she left a note pinned on the door of her room.

"Dear Pat," she had written, "I am sorry you saw my messy room that first day and I am very thankful you came back after I had cleaned it up. I am going to try to keep it neat and prove to you and my parents that I have accepted the responsibility for keeping it in order. Then maybe you will know I can give you good care, too."

This went on for two weeks. Notes between Lucy and Pat were exchanged each day. Neither her father nor her mother said a word about them. By now Lucy had formed the habit of caring for her clothes and her room. Then one day her father drove her and Trudy to the swimming pool and said with an amused smile, "Perhaps we'd better stop at the store for some birdseed on our way home. You just might need it."

Lucy smiled at Trudy and moved close to her father. "Oh," was all she could say.

All the time she was in the pool she was thinking of Pat, the Parakeet. "Do you suppose he'll be there when I get home?" she asked Trudy.

"Oh, I hope so," answered Trudy.

"I do, too," said Lucy. "Daddy surely hinted it, didn't he?"

Later, as Lucy opened the door of her room, she stopped still. There perched in an attractive green and white cage was Pat, the beautiful parakeet. It seemed to Lucy that he was almost grinning at her.

"But parakeets don't grin," she said to herself, laughing. She ran over to the cage. "Oh, you beautiful, beautiful bird," she exclaimed. Pat actually answered her with a nod of his head, or so Lucy thought.

That night she very carefully covered his cage with one of Mother's large towels, and in the morning she cleaned the cage and gave him fresh seed and water. "I'll never, never let your cage stay messy," she promised. "And I'll never let my room be messy either," she added, as she went about making her bed and straightening up. Pat said something which Lucy did not quite understand.

Then one morning, after Lucy had had Pat about a week, her friend Trudy called very early. "We're going to reunion for the day," she said. "Can you go with us?"

Lucy called to her mother and was given consent to

go. She started to throw things right and left, for Trudy had said they would be along in about an hour.

"Goodness, your room!" exclaimed her mother as she came in. "It's a mess."

Just then Pat spoke up. "Messy, messy, messy," he repeated over and over. Lucy suddenly remembered. She had forgotten to clean his cage.

"Oh, dear me," she said. "Please forgive me, Pat. I'll soon have you all cleaned up." She went to work and in a few minutes everything was in order both in his cage and in her room.

"Well, Lucy," said her mother just as Trudy's daddy drove up, "you have certainly proved that you are growing up. I am the proudest mother in the whole, wide world." Lucy went out the door with a happy heart.

59

RUSS FINDS A NEW FRIEND

"Mother, guess what! We have a new boy at school. His name is Otis Brown, and he is just my age. He can catch a ball better than any of us."

Russ's mother looked up from the pan of apples she was peeling. "Fine. Now you will have a new friend," she remarked.

"I don't know about that," said Russ slowly as he reached for a piece of apple. "You know I've been the best catcher in school and to have another boy come in and beat me isn't fun."

"Why, Russ, what a thing to say."

Russ looked ashamed. "I was hasty, but, Mom, it was hard to see all the guys pounding him on the back and bragging him up. I was—well, I was—"

"A wee bit jealous?" suggested his mother.

"I suppose that's what you'd call it," admitted Russ, "though it doesn't sound nice when you say it out loud. But I haven't told you everything, Mom. Otis is a—a—a Negro."

180

Russ's mother stood up. She carried her pan of peeled apples to the sink and ran clear water over them. Finally she turned to Russ, whose red hair and brown freckles shone in the late afternoon sun. His face was pale. He twirled his cap nervously.

"I know what you're thinking," he told her. "His color has nothing whatever to do with it. I know it doesn't, but it just isn't fair to be beaten by a Negro." He rubbed his eyes to keep back angry tears, and turned and ran out the back door.

Russ's mother prayed, "Help him, Lord, please. Help him to understand what you meant when you gave your two great commandments. Help him to see that he and Otis Brown have you as their heavenly Father, which makes them brothers."

Russ walked slowly over to the vacant lot where the boys gathered after school for ball practice. The usual gang was there. The happy face of Otis Brown stood out among the others.

"Come on, Russ," he called. "Take my place, will you? It looks like a storm is coming up and I've got a job to do for my mother before it starts to rain."

For a moment Russ was tempted to refuse. "I'll not play second fiddle to a Negro," he wanted to say. But for some reason the words would not come. He looked at Otis—at his big, happy grin—and he said to himself, "Why, he is a real guy. I wonder where he lives. I wonder if he goes to church. I wonder what I have learned about being a missionary."

"Okay," he said, just as a dark cloud began spilling its rain in big oval drops.

"Boy, oh, boy!" yelled Spike, the captain. "Maybe

we'd all better race for our club shack until the rain stops. Come on, Russ and Otis. Let's run."

"But I have to hurry home," said Otis. "The clothes are on the line, and they'll get all wet."

"I'll help you," Russ offered.

"Oh, that will be super," Otis said.

Soon the boys came to a neat cottage with green shutters. Russ could see the clothes blowing on the line. They were protected some from the rain by a huge maple tree, but it was just beginning to leaf, and he could see it wouldn't be long before they would be wet.

"Here," said Otis handing him a basket. "I'll grab them and you stuff them in the basket."

As they worked the clouds lifted and the April shower ceased as suddenly as it had begun. The boys laughed.

"Well, anyway, they're all off the line," said Otis. "Now come into the house with me, Russ."

As they walked toward the back door Russ was wondering why Otis' mother had not taken the clothes in.

"This is Mom, Russ," said Otis as they stepped into the kitchen. A sweet-faced woman smiled up at Russ from a wheelchair.

In the back of his mind Russ could see a picture that had never meant much to him before—a picture of Jesus with his arm around the shoulders of a colored boy. Russ's heart seemed to be singing. He could hardly wait to get home and tell his mother about the new friend he had found.

60

HOW SUSAN PROVED HER LOVE

Susan was not doing so well at school. Her eyes were giving her trouble. One day her parents had a long talk with her teacher.

"I think you should take her to a school in Iowa City," the teacher told them. "She cannot read her lessons, which makes it very hard for her. This is a special school for children who have eye trouble."

"But Iowa City is miles away from Creston!" cried Susan, when her parents talked it over with her. "Why, I'll never get home!"

"Oh, yes, you will," they comforted. "There will be Thanksgiving and Christmas and summer vacation. It will be for only two years."

"Two years!" exclaimed Susan. "It seems forever."

Susan knew it was the thing to do, however, so very reluctantly she agreed to go. Soon she found herself in a strange town, a strange home, and a strange school. The teachers were kind to her, and so were Mr. and Mrs. Benton with whom she lived. But Susan was very homesick. In all her twelve years this was the first time she had been away from home for more than a few days at a time. She thought about her homesickness most of the time and felt sorry for herself. One day, when a letter came from home with her allowance in it, Susan started to cry.

"I just wish I could take this money and buy a ticket for home," she sobbed, trying to keep back the tears. "I'm so lonely."

Mrs. Benton put a hand on her shoulder. "My dear, I wish you wouldn't feel this way. You are doing so well at school and your mother and daddy are so happy about the reports they get from your teachers. It must be hard for them to know that you are not happy. You love them, don't you?"

"Oh, yes," Susan assured her. "I do. I do. I love them and my brother Bobbie and little Jeanie." And then she sighed. "But I miss them and I miss my church friends."

Mrs. Benton had already heard about Susan's church, the Reorganized Church of Jesus Christ of Latter Day Saints. Susan had told her even more than she cared to hear. "Let us not discuss it," she had said once and wondered with a guilty conscience if this was one of the reasons Susan was unhappy. But she said nothing.

That night, after the house was still, Susan lay in her bed thinking of home. She thought of her mother and daddy, brother Bobbie, and little Jeanie. She thought of

184

the little baby brother whom she had never seen. He was the first baby and had died at birth. Mother and Daddy had said he was such a beautiful baby. Then she remembered a part of a conversation she had heard one day.

Daddy had said, "We can use the money we had saved for a marker for baby's grave."

"Yes, that is what we'll have to do," Mother agreed.

Somehow Susan knew they had been discussing the extra expense of sending her to school. Suddenly her heart was filled with love for them and the baby whom she had never seen. And then it was just as if a voice spoke to her heart: "Prove your love, my child."

"How, dear God?" she answered back, for she seemed to know that he had spoken.

And then a wonderful idea came to her. "I'll save some of my allowance each week," she decided. "When I have enough I'll buy a marker for little brother's grave. And I'll write cheerful letters home. That will surely prove my love." Susan dropped off to sleep with a smile upon her face.

It was not always easy to save. There were so many ways to spend money—candy and gum and ice-cream cones, skating and movies. However, she never forgot the night she had had that great joy in her heart, so each day it became easier for her to do without some of the things she did not really need. She began shopping around. There were several places in Iowa City where tombstones were sold, and Susan became familiar with all of them.

Although she did not write a word of the wonderful secret to the family they soon realized that she was much more contented. Her letters were cheerful accounts of school and the friends she was making. In one letter she had mentioned how difficult it was to tell the Bentons about the gospel, and her parents had warned her not to antagonize them. "Just show by your life that you have something very lovely and worthwhile," they wrote.

The year was soon over and Susan was home for the summer. Her family found her much more thoughtful and kind, always finding things to do for others. When school began in the fall, Susan could hardly wait to see everyone, especially the Bentons. "They are my other mother and daddy," she told her parents.

Susan went right on saving her money. The amount grew larger and larger but she had learned that a grave marker cost a lot of money. One day she confided in Mrs. Benton.

"Why, child, my brother is in that business. I'll talk to him the very next time I see him."

Surely enough, Mrs. Benton's brother had just the thing and Susan found she would have enough money by the time school was out. She was too happy for words. That night, when she had her talk with God, she said, "Oh, thank you, thank you! Now if I could just share my church with the Bentons I'd be the happiest girl in all the world."

The Bentons had noticed the growth Susan had made. They had seen her reading her church books and had said they would like to visit her church. One weekend they even took her home and attended church on Sunday. "You have a very friendly church," they said later. Susan was happy but not satisfied.

And then the time came when her stay in Iowa City was coming to a close. Her teachers had said she was ready to take up her schoolwork at home. Plans were made for the Bentons to take her a part of the way home with the marker in the trunk of the car. They were to meet her family in Ottumwa. The Bentons and Susan arrived first and when they saw her folks drive up Susan was out of the car like a flash of lightning. She could hardly wait to show them her surprise.

"Look!" she exclaimed, opening the trunk of the Bentons' car.

It took a few minutes for Susan's mother and daddy to speak.

"Why, child," was all they could say, as they hugged her close to them.

"I wanted to prove my love," she explained.

"You have a lovely daughter," said Mrs. Benton, putting her arm around Susan.

"Yes," said Susan's daddy. "I can see that not only have her eyes improved but she has learned that thinking of others is the best way to prove one's love."

As the little family drove home that afternoon after a picnic with the Bentons, they talked of how very much God had blessed them.

"And someday," sighed Susan happily, "I hope my other mother and daddy learn to love God's church." Susan was still thinking of others.

61

DICK
WAS
HONEST

Dick found the long package on his way home from school February 21. It was all rolled up in a piece of brown wrapping paper. As he opened it his eyes danced.

"Just what I need," he told himself, unrolling a beautiful silk flag. "Now I can march in the George Washington parade tomorrow." The bright red and blue shone out against the snowy white. It was just like the flag he had seen in the store, only he had lacked fifteen cents of having enough money to buy it. He had been saving his allowance for several weeks. "If only I had not spent some of it for candy," he had told himself sorrowfully. But now everything was working out for him.

"Am I lucky!" he repeated over and over as he hurried for home.

The house was empty. Dick remembered that his mother had said she would be at the church for women's meeting. He ran down the hall to his room and carefully placed the flag in the top dresser drawer. Then went to the kitchen for a lunch of milk and graham crackers. As he ate he could see himself leading the flag parade through all the other rooms. Each room was to have a special stunt. He could just hear the boys and girls saying, "Dick has the biggest and the nicest flag of all!"

The boy's thoughts were interrupted by the ringing of the telephone. Just as he got up to answer he heard the front door open.

"Mom?" he called.

"Yes, dear."

"Telephone."

His mother hurried to answer. Dick listened. "No, I don't think so, but wait a minute. I'll ask him. He's right here." She turned to Dick. "It's Mrs. Roth, son. She lost a package . . . a long, slim one. She thinks she dropped it on the walk somewhere near her house. She had been shopping for a flag and did not get home with it. Did you find it, dear?"

Dick's picture of himself leading the parade grew dim for a moment. He seemed to hear two voices speaking to him. One was saying, *Honesty is the best policy. Honesty is the best policy.* The other voice was saying, *Finders are keepers. You needn't say anything. Mother will think you bought the flag yourself. She knows you have been saving your money.*

While the battle was going on within him he heard his mother answering Mrs. Roth.

"I guess Dick didn't find it. I'm terribly sorry." She waited a moment. "Oh, that's too bad. I just know how disappointed Peter must be. Well, if we hear of anyone finding it I'll let you know. Good-bye." She turned from the telephone. "Poor Peter," she said. "He had such plans. I have an idea. Dick, why don't you go out and look for the package? Maybe it got pushed off the walk and into the bushes. With Peter's leg in a cast he can't do it, you know."

"What did he want of a flag, anyway?" queried Dick, as he turned toward the door. "He can't march."

"Why, his mother said he had saved his money to buy it and had intended lending it to some boy who hadn't been able to buy one for himself—Freddy Walters, probably. He has had a hard time of it, you know, with no daddy. Run along, son. Play you are a detective. How about it?"

Dick left the house halfheartedly. He knew how silly it was to look for the flag. He walked up and down the street aimlessly, kicking at the bushes which lined the walk. When he saw his father turning into their driveway he hurried home.

"I can tell by your face that you didn't find it," said his mother as he came into the house. "Well, it's too bad. I hope it shows up. Get washed for supper, son. You know how hungry Daddy always is, and you, too."

His father opened the door. "Hungry? I'll say, and something certainly smells good, too." He gave Dick a pat on the back and went over to the table where Dick's mother was placing a steaming casserole. "How about a kiss from the cook?" he asked, grinning.

Dick looked at them. He knew how they trusted him. Suddenly he felt sick through and through. "I guess I won't eat anything," he told them. "I . . . I . . . I don't feel very hungry."

"*You* not hungry!" exclaimed his father.

"Why, son, you're always as empty as . . . well, it's usually like filling a silo."

190

"You better try to eat a little, Dick," remonstrated his mother.

"I can't eat. I don't feel like it. I'm going to my room," he answered, turning and almost running down the hall.

"I'd better take his temperature, don't you think?" asked his mother with a worried frown. "Here, we'll sit down and have the blessing on the food and then you start eating. I'll go see about him."

Dick had opened his dresser drawer to look at the flag again. He felt of the soft silk. He practiced carrying it back and forth in front of the full-length mirror on his closet door. He tried to sing the flag song softly, the one that told about George Washington, the father of his country. When he came to the words, "and the story does not die; he never, never told a lie," Dick stopped suddenly. "He never, never told a lie," he repeated. All at once he could not bear to look at his reflection in the mirror. He dropped the flag in a heap and ran to his bed, throwing himself across it just as his mother came in.

She saw the crumpled flag lying on the floor.

"Why, son, you bought your flag, didn't you? Good!" she exclaimed. "But why is it here on the floor? This is no way to treat the symbol of our wonderful country." She stooped to pick it up, folding it neatly.

Dick sat up, watching her for a moment. His face was pale. He knew what he had to do. "Mother—I—that—that is not *my* flag. I—I—" Finally the whole story was out. "I am so ashamed, Mother, but I feel a lot better. I even feel I can eat now—that is, as soon as I call Mrs. Roth." He did not wait for his mother to answer. He flew down the hall.

Dick did not spare himself. He told Peter's mother

the whole story from start to finish. "It was wrong, Mrs. Roth, and I just hope you can forgive me."

"Peter will want you to carry his flag, I know," Mrs. Roth told him.

"No, I think Freddy should carry it," insisted Dick. "Anyhow, I have a different idea. I'm going to make a banner to carry. I'm going to print on it in big, big letters 'Honesy is the best policy,' and I just hope I never, *never* forget it!"

Dick's mother and father smiled happily at each other as he came toward the table singing, "And the story does not die; he never, never told a lie."

"I don't know whether that old story about George and the cherry tree is true or not," remarked his father, serving himself a second helping from the casserole, "but it surely is true that honesty pays, son."

Dick smiled. "It helps the appetite, too, Dad. Say, why don't you fill up my plate before you eat everything on the table?"

62

HOW THE SCOTTS FOUND GOD

Rudy Scott was thinking hard as he walked out of the assembly hall that bleak November day. It was Wednesday afternoon and Thanksgiving was the following day.

"And what have I to be thankful for?" he muttered. When the speaker at assembly had advised them to list their blessings he had inwardly scoffed. It seemed that all *he'd* had for the past several months had been hard knocks . . . he and his mother and father. First his dad had become ill and was unable to work. Now his mother was worn out taking care of Dad. It made Rudy's heart ache every time he looked at her tired, drawn face and calloused hands. She was almost sick, too . . . sick with sorrow. All the savings were gone and now the only money coming in was what he earned at the grocery store after school. And they wouldn't accept charity! They were too proud for that.

"Thanksgiving. Bah!" he said to himself, hurrying through the hall and out the door to his bicycle. What else was it the old fellow had said? Oh yes, something about "our extremity is God's opportunity." Mom and Dad never spent much time at church. Something had happened a long time before he was born. But even if they didn't they were as good as could be. They always said that God helped those who helped themselves.

"But they've done all they can, and so have I. Where is God anyway? If you're up there in the sky can't you see we need you? Why don't you do something about it? Please, God," Rudy prayed.

Rudy felt better for some reason. Could it be because he'd gone to God with his problem? As he pushed the broom back and forth in the grocery store he kept thinking about it. It was just as if "Someone" had heard.

At seven o'clock he told his employer good-night and hopped on his bike for home. He was hungry as a bear. The boss had told him to eat some cheese and crackers for a lunch after school, but he said he would wait until he got home. He wasn't going to have anyone think he needed a handout. Mom would have something warm for him to eat. No matter how cross Dad had been because of his pain nor how weary she was, he never came home to an empty table.

But he wondered what there would be tonight. He had seen the refrigerator that morning and he knew the cupboard shelves were almost bare. Why, even the soup beans were almost gone. The fruit jars his mother had filled were nearly all empty now. My, but he was empty, too. It seemed he hadn't been really filled up in days.

"I could eat a cow," Rudy muttered as he opened the back door. The aroma of good food cooking almost took his breath. "Wow!" he exclaimed, tossing his cap on the hook behind the door and heading for the sink to wash his hands. His exclamation had brought his mother from the other part of the house. Rudy looked at her in surprise. Her eyes were shining.

"Son," she said happily. "I . . ."

Rudy interrupted her. "What gives, Mom? Where did you get it?" He motioned toward the stove.

"Oh, Rudy, you'll never believe this, but it's true. About five o'clock this afternoon wonderful things began happening around here. Now sit down and eat. I'll dish up for you and tell you all about it."

"Wait a minute," he remonstrated. "I won't eat a bite until I know how you got it. I don't want any food that's been begged for . . . not if I starve. How's Dad? I'll go in to see him first." He started toward the bedroom.

"But wait, son. Your father is much better and right now he is sleeping. Please sit down and let me tell you. And look . . ." She opened the refrigerator door. Rudy hadn't seen so much food in their refrigerator in many a day . . . a huge turkey, sweet potatoes, celery, carrots, cranberries, ice cream—everything to make a Thanksgiving dinner. "And see here," his mother went on as she threw open the cupboard doors. There were well-stocked shelves which only that morning had been almost bare. Rudy just stared. The fragrance coming from a bubbling kettle on the stove was almost more than he could take, too.

"Tell me, Mom. Tell me before I lose all my will-power and start in on this . . . this manna from heaven." He suddenly remembered that the old gentleman had told a story about manna at assembly.

Mrs. Scott smiled. "Manna from heaven. That's exactly what it is, my boy. It's God's answer to prayer. And don't be afraid to eat it, for he provided it."

195

"How? Did he just open up the sky and drop it down?"

"Almost. Let me explain. You see, this man . . ."

"*What* man?"

"Oh, I forgot. Let me start at the beginning."

"Please do."

"Son, when you left this morning I knew I had to do something. I was desperate. I finally found myself on my knees and I was praying . . . I, who didn't even know if I believed in God. Then after I had poured out my needs to him I arose and somehow I felt sure that he had heard and that he knew. I felt that everything would be taken care of and I even sang as I worked. Then when I went in to care for Dad he was smiling. Why, I hadn't seen him smile in months." Rudy's mother paused to wipe the tears from her eyes. " 'Mother,' he said to me, 'do you remember I've told you about that man who worked with me in the factory, the one who has invited us to his church at different times? Well, I want you to call him and ask him to come over. He'll come, I know he will, even if I was rather rude to him at the factory. You see, I had a dream in which I saw him and another man (they are elders in their church) standing at my bedside praying. I want to see him, Mother.' Rudy," continued his mother, "I called this man, Mr. Peters, and he and a friend came about five o'clock. They talked awhile, then administered to him."

"Administered? What's that?"

"It's like it says in the Bible (I remember reading it in the book of James). They anointed your father's head with oil which had been consecrated; they placed their hands on his head, and then they prayed such sincere prayers. And, son, it was like a miracle. Dad seemed to rally almost immediately. Mr. Peters said it was a testimony for us."

Rudy's fists were in his eyes. "Mother . . . I . . . I . . ."

"Don't be ashamed to cry, son. I'm afraid we've all been stubborn at the Scott house."

"And the food?" asked Rudy. "Did you tell them?"

"No, not one word about our circumstances. The men left in a few minutes and soon after Mr. Peters and his wife came. My, I never saw such big baskets filled with food. They assured us that if we were like them, when sickness came we could make use of it. They said it was just a friendly gesture extended among their people and that we'd have our turn, if we wanted it, to help someone else someday. They made it sound as if it would be selfish not to accept." Rudy's mother had spooned a generous helping of beef stew on his plate. "Now eat, my boy, and be thankful that God hears and answers prayers."

"He sure does, Mom. Want to know something? I prayed, too. Oh, I was pretty ugly at first, but I had to pray. I think he must have heard me, too." Rudy reached for another slice of bread and buttered it as he went on with the telling of his experience.

"Well, I think it's about time the Scotts mend their ways, son," said his mother with feeling. "I've promised our friends we'll start to church as soon as we can. Dad is so much better already that he says he'll be there Sunday. I doubt if he can go quite so soon but maybe one of us can."

"Yes," agreed Rudy. "I guess like that man at assembly said, 'our extremity is God's opportunity.'"

His mother answered, "Yes, God does help those who help themselves, but we must learn to accept his help when he gives it. We need to be more humble, son."

Just then a voice was heard from the bedroom. "Come on in here. I want to talk, too, and I'm hungry again. Bring on the stew." Rudy and his mother smiled happily. With arms around each other they joined Rudy's father. Surely this would be the nicest Thanksgiving they had ever had.

63

GRANDMA'S
EXTRA
HANDS AND FEET

Dick and Brenda were twins. They lived with their mother and father on a shady street lined with pretty houses. Just across the street from their house lived an old woman. She lived all alone except for Rascal, her calico cat. Everyone called this old woman "Grandma." She wasn't a really truly Grandma to everyone in the neighborhood. She was really Mrs. Smith.

Grandma's house was very old. She had lived in it for more than sixty years, and she liked her little old house. The twins' mother once asked her why she did not move into the old ladies' home. "Then you wouldn't have to carry out ashes. It would be much easier for you."

"But I like to do those things," the old woman answered with a chuckle. "I've done them all my life. If I went away my little house would miss me. Rascal would miss me, too. And I would miss them and all my good neighbors."

"And we'd miss you," the twins' mother assured her, and everything went along as usual. Then one day when

Grandma went out to the pump for a bucket of water she tripped and fell. It was hard for her to get up because she was quite a large woman and she had stiff knees. After several tries, however, she made it and went limping into the house holding her left wrist in her right hand.

Now the twins' mother, who was hanging freshly washed clothes on the line, had not seen Grandma fall, but she did see her hobbling into the house. She called to the twins, who were playing cowboy in the yard.

"Dick and Brenda, run over to Grandma's and see if she is all right, please. I thought I saw her limping as she went into the house just now."

The twins hurried across the street on their make-believe horses. When they called at Grandma's door she did not answer in her usual cheery voice. She asked them to come in, however, and there she sat in her rocker by the window. She was looking at her right foot and holding her left wrist in her right hand.

"What's the matter, Grandma?" asked Dick.

"Are you hurt?" queried Brenda.

Grandma told them about her fall. "And, children, I think I have a broken toe and a broken wrist."

"A broken toe!" exclaimed Dick.

"A broken wrist!" exclaimed Brenda.

"Yes, I'm afraid so. I think I'll need to go to the doctor as soon as possible."

"Mother will take you," the twins both said at once. And then Dick added, "I'll go right over now and tell her." He went dashing out the door.

"I'll stay and help you get ready," offered Brenda.

"That will be fine, child," Grandma told her. "You may be my feet and hands."

Soon Brenda had Grandma ready to go. The twins'

mother drove her car up the driveway as close to the front door as she could get. They all helped Grandma into the car.

"Look after Rascal and my little house," said Grandma.

"We will," the twins promised her.

When they had gone Dick said, "I'll finish Grandma's chores for her."

"And I'll wash up her dishes, make her bed, and dust the house," said Brenda.

Just then Rascal came slipping out from under the bed. "Meow, meow," she mewed.

"I think she's hungry," said Dick. "Let's feed her."

"Meow, meow," mewed Rascal, and she ate every bit of the bread and milk Brenda put into her little blue saucer by the stove.

The twins were so busy that it seemed no time before they heard their mother's car.

"Why, where's Grandma?" they chorused.

"I took her to the hospital."

"The hospital?" they exclaimed. Then Dick asked, "Was her toe really broken?"

"And her wrist? Was it really broken, too?" inquired Brenda.

"Yes," said their mother. "They were both broken. The doctor X-rayed her toe and put it in a splint. Then he X-rayed her wrist and put her arm in a cast. He said it had been quite a shock to Grandma and that she had better stay where he could watch her for a while."

"Will she get to come home tomorrow?" asked Brenda.

The twins' mother put an arm around each of them. "I think that depends on you, Dick and Brenda," she said thoughtfully. "Are you willing to be hands and feet for Grandma for a while?"

"Yes, yes, yes," they responded.

"She really wants to be in her little house," explained their mother. "She almost cried at the thought of not coming home, poor dear. But, children," she went on, "this will mean a lot of extra work for you. Of course it will show how much you really love Grandma."

"I love her a lot," said Dick.

"Enough to do her chores when the other boys want you to go swimming or play ball?"

Dick thought for a moment. He tossed his cowboy hat up in the air two or three times before he answered. But when he did, his voice was determined. "Why, I can play ball any old time. I want to be Grandma's hands and feet."

"I love her, too," Brenda said emphatically. "I love her enough to leave my dolls and other play when she needs me."

Grandma came home the next day. She looked about the little house as if she had not seen it for a long time. On the table was a lunch that Brenda had prepared—a bowl of vegetable soup, an apple and carrot salad, some cookies, and a glass of milk. Grandma ate every crumb. Then Brenda washed up the dishes. Dick ran errands. Grandma moved around with a crutch and was as happy as could be. Rascal mewed and purred.

Finally the day came when the doctor took off the toe splint. Grandma wriggled her toe for a while and it worked just like the other ones. Another day came and he took the cast off her arm. It was a bit stiff, but she soon had it limbered up.

"God bless you, dear children," said Grandma gratefully. "If it had not been for you I couldn't have stayed in my own little house. I thank you with all my heart."

64

CHEERS FOR CLAUDIA

Pretty Claudia Jeffries sat at the desk in her room with a pencil in her hand. Her English assignment lay before her but she had not even started on it. Claudia was going over in her mind something that had happened at school that afternoon and was having a battle with herself. Coming home at four she had paused only long enough to call "Hi, Mom," as she dashed through the hall and up the stairs, not even answering back when her mother had asked, "Don't you want a glass of milk and some cookies, dear?" With extreme effort Claudia had refrained from slamming the door of her room.

It was a pleasant room. Only a few weeks before she and her mother had redecorated it. The walls were a bright geranium red. With the white ceiling and shag rugs they made a striking contrast. Frilly white tiebacks hung at the two windows with drapes of red and white stripes. The bedspread and dressing table skirt were of the same striped material. Books lined a part of the wall. The pictures, especially the "Head of Christ" which hung above her desk, were in direct contrast to her present ugly mood. Claudia was reminded of the dedication service she had had when the room was finished. Her three closest friends had been there, girls she had known since kindergarten days. That night they had given her the picture of Jesus. And Ardis Moore, to whom she was directing many of her bitter thoughts, was one of those girls.

"I hate myself for the way I am acting," Claudia muttered to herself. "Surely a girl almost sixteen should be old enough to know she can't have everything her own way. Well, at least I didn't go crying to Mom. I'll lick this thing." Usually Claudia enjoyed writing themes, but today the blank sheet before her held no appeal. Her short, brown, curly hair needed its weekly shampoo. There were buttons to be sewed on the new white organdy blouse that lay across the bed. She had made it under her mother's supervision, except for the buttonholes. I should call down and thank her, she thought. But instead, here I sit, like a . . . like a . . . well, like a goose!

She pressed her hands to her temples. Her head ached. "I've got to learn to make the best of disappointments," she said to herself. "What was it the Zion's League leader said the other night? Something about growing up. Oh, yes. Learn to act your age. I suppose I'm acting like a two-year-old. But I was so sure of the leading part in that play, and it just wasn't fair of Miss Griffin to give it to Ardis after letting me think I was to have it. Oh, I know she explained that Ardis was more the type, but haven't I always done my parts well and haven't I a much better speaking voice?" Tears of self-pity welled up in Claudia's eyes as she let her head drop to the desk. "I'm crying just like a baby. Why, I doubt if I'm even a two-year-old. About six months, probably."

She reached for a tissue and wiped her eyes. With another one she blew her nose. "If Mother hears me she'll be up here." She made herself get up and walk over to the dressing table. "What a sight you are!" she said disgustedly to the girl in the mirror. Her usually sparkling brown eyes were red with weeping. "Crying doesn't improve anyone's looks, that's sure," she continued. "Well, I may as well wash my hair. There will just be time for that and my English before Mother calls me to set the table for supper." She glanced at her watch as she laid it upon the table and picked up her brush. At the one hundredth stroke she went whistling into the bathroom. It was not a very animated tune. Sounds like a funeral dirge, Claudia thought, chuckling in spite of herself. But at least I am trying.

The water felt good to her aching head. She dug into her scalp as she lathered it, rinsed, lathered, rinsed, and rinsed again. The job of putting it up in rollers was only a matter of a few minutes. Then tying a red scarf around her head Claudia went back to her desk. The assignment for English was finished just as she heard her mother call.

"Coming," Claudia answered back. "I'll sew those buttons on the blouse after the dishes tonight," she reflected, running down the stairs.

An inviting aroma welcomed her as she entered the gay green and white kitchen. Her mother was at the sink preparing vegetables for a salad. A kettle of stew bubbled on the stove. "Umm! It smells good out here. I'm starved!" To herself she admitted, "Why, I am hungry. And I thought I could never eat again."

Mrs. Jeffries had a pleasant face, the kind that people seemed to trust the very moment they saw her. A light shone in her soft gray eyes. "I'm glad to hear that you are hungry," she said, smiling. "When you went up to your room with hardly a nod I was a bit worried. I thought of coming up with the thermometer but decided against it. There are times, I know, when we just prefer our own company."

Claudia went over to the cupboard and took out plates and silverware to place on the table in the dining room. "I'm sorry, Mother," she said. "It was rude of me."

"Oh, that was all right, dear. I just wondered." After a brief pause she asked, "How did things go at school today?"

"You wouldn't be prying, would you, Mother?" questioned Claudia, laughing.

Mrs. Jeffries grinned. "I know that something is wrong and the sooner you get it off your chest the better you'll feel. Come on. What is it?"

Claudia stopped on her way to the table with four tumblers in her hands. Her father and twin brother Bill would be home from the grocery store in a few minutes. Mr. Jeffries owned and operated the Serve Right Market and Bill worked for him before and after school.

"I might as well get it out of my system before the menfolk come home," she sighed. "Males just don't appreciate temperamental women."

She walked over to the sink and planted a kiss on her mother's cheek. Then she sat down on one corner of the worktable. "It sounds silly but—well—you know how I've been depending on that part in the play. And to put it briefly, when the parts were handed out today I discovered that I am to be the maid! The maid! Imagine that! And Ardis Moore has the lead! Mother, I've just been having an awful fight with myself. I've felt as if I just couldn't stand to be so humiliated."

Mrs. Jeffries shredded the remainder of the head of lettuce before she made any comment. Then she asked quietly, "Have you thought of what it must mean to Ardis?"

Claudia looked at her mother in astonishment. "Why, what a strange thing to say! Can't you put yourself in my place? Don't you want me to be happy?"

"Claudia, you know how you and I stand. Your happiness means everything to me. However, if you think I'm going to shed any tears because you did not get the leading part in that play you are mistaken. I am much more interested in your reaction to disappointments than I am about your never being disappointed. I am concerned about how you acted toward Miss Griffin and Ardis. I'm anxious that you grow up in your relationships with people."

"Yes, I know," interrupted Claudia. "You want me to act my age. And I've been trying, Mother, honestly I have, only I'm afraid I didn't once try to put myself in Ardis' place."

"There are many times, dear, all through life when we meet situations which at first are not as we had anticipated. But let us analyze this one for a bit. Think of Ardis. Think of her background. Put yourself in her place. Can't you just feel her happiness? Has she ever been anything but gracious over your many successes ever since you were youngsters together? Think of what this must mean to her. And now would you spoil it all for her?"

"Why, Mother, you make it all so different. I can see that I was only thinking of myself. I . . .," but before

Claudia could finish they heard the front door slam and voices in the hall. "Anything to eat around this house? We are two hungry men."

"Dinner is served, sirs," Claudia called back.

Mr. Jeffries was a slight man with kind brown eyes. Bill resembled him. They both came sniffing into the kitchen. "Shall we stay?" said the man with a grin.

"Yes, let's do," his son decided. "I sort of like the looks of the cooks, too."

"Quit your kidding, you two," spoke up Claudia, "and get ready to eat."

A few minutes later Bill remarked, "Ardis was in the store after school, Claud."

"That's nice," the girl answered back with a knowing look. "That wasn't hard for you to take, was it?" It was common knowledge that Bill thought Ardis was a pretty nice girl.

"I was complimenting her on her successful tryout for the play. She was so happy about it," Bill went on, pretending to ignore the gentle ribbing. "One thing bothered her, though, Sis. She told me she would rather not have the part than to have it make a difference in your friendship. I laughed and said, 'Oh, Claud is too intelligent to be jealous. She's tops!' And then Ardis said a very peculiar thing."

"What did she say, Bill?" Claudia put the question with a noticeable effort, her face pale.

"She said you hadn't said one word to her afterwards. She said you brushed past her in the locker room and scurried out the door as if you were furious. She was almost crying when she told me."

Claudia burst into tears. "All right, rub it in. I did

just that. I was little, mean, and despicable, and I am ashamed. I hate myself!" She tried to keep back the tears.

Bill looked bewildered as he went on. "Well, now that I have made the incision I might as well go on and operate. Ardis was plenty concerned about it. She said she would give a lot just to hear your voice over the phone saying that everything is just as it used to be between you two."

There was an uncomfortable silence in the room. Mrs. Jeffries served the dessert. It was apple cobbler, a favorite with the family, but no one touched it. Finally Mr. Jeffries spoke.

"Son, I think you have been a bit rough on your sister. It isn't always easy to grow up. Some people never do. They go through life holding grudges, feeling slights, wanting everything their own way, never developing the Christlike attitude. You haven't always taken your defeats in the field of sports as you should either. Perhaps it would be well to apologize."

"Aw, shucks, Dad. When I started off I never dreamed Ardis was right about the deal. I thought she only imagined it. I just didn't know how much a part in a play meant to girls. I'm sorry, Sis."

"I had it coming to me, Bill," Claudia said, wiping her eyes. "I didn't want to feel that way, but for the life of me I couldn't shake the feeling. I had a long talk with myself, and then when Mother and I talked it over she helped me a lot. By the time you started in on me I was already fed up with my attitude, and had asked God's forgiveness." She jumped up from the table. "Excuse me, please."

"Hey, where are you going, chick?" asked her father. "Let's eat our cobbler."

"I'll be back, Dad. I have a telephone call to make."

"Three cheers for Claudia!" Bill called after her.

As Claudia dialed the Moores' number she felt as if a great load had been lifted from her shoulders. "I'm glad Bill made that incision," She said to herself. "This growing up isn't so bad after all." With a happy and peaceful heart she waited for the voice of her friend in answer to her call.

65

A
FRIEND
INDEED

The story Claudia had heard about Enid at school that day had shocked her more than she could say. Enid Carson was one of her best friends. "It just can't be true," Claudia reasoned with herself. "Why, she wouldn't steal. She just couldn't!"

As she headed toward home, Claudia tried to reach some plausible explanation for the news that had spread about Enid. She walked along dejectedly. Her feet felt like bags of lead.

"Anyway," she stormed within herself, "why don't I just forget it? Enid hasn't been too friendly lately since she has been running with those other girls—girls who think clothes and style and such things are the most important part of life." Claudia had been a bit disappointed to see that Enid's sense of values had changed, too. "But she is still my friend and I just don't believe this about her."

She was approaching the city library and decided to stop in for a while. "Maybe I can think of something," she said to herself. To her consternation, just as she turned in she saw Enid coming down the steps. They looked into each other's eyes. Enid was an attractive girl with honey-blonde hair tied back with a blue ribbon which matched the blue of her eyes. She was Claudia's height and age, neatly dressed, a girl who had always warranted the respect and admiration of her friends.

Claudia reached out her hand. "Enid, I don't believe it," she began. "Tell me, please, how you could be under such suspicion. Won't you let me walk along home with you?" She tried to link her arm in Enid's but the girl pulled away.

"Claudia, it's no use. I haven't a chance," she sobbed. Like a frightened child she hurried down the street. Claudia stood and looked longingly toward her, then sighed and went on up the steps of the library. Searching for a secluded place where she might be alone with her unhappy thoughts she aimlessly selected a magazine from the rack and settled in a far corner near the classics.

It was a perfect day. As Claudia thumbed the pages of the magazine she was attracted by a robin that had lighted on a branch of the soft maple just outside the window. It sang so lustily that several people looked up and smiled.

How can anyone dare to smile, thought Claudia, when Enid is in such trouble? And then she reflected, "But, of course, they don't know yet. The paper won't be out for several hours. But then everyone will be talking about it. I can just hear them. And I can just see the heading in the paper: 'Local Girl Caught Stealing.'" In her mind's eye she was reading all the shocking details.

Suddenly Claudia jumped to her feet. "I wonder what

she was doing here in the library. You would think a girl accused of stealing would want to hide her face. There's a lot I don't understand. I've got to do something."

She hurried to close the magazine when she noticed a story title. "Fair-weather Friends," she read. Claudia read this over several times, then with a look of determination in her eyes she hastily returned the magazine to its place in the rack and fled out the door.

"Maybe there's time for me to be more than a fair-weather friend," she declared. "I'll talk it over with Mother. Oh, thank you, God, for Mother."

Mrs. Jeffries, Claudia's mother, was weeding a flower bed when her daughter turned into the yard. She had a happy, contented look upon her face as she knelt among the brightly colored tulips.

"Mother, I've something to tell you that just can't wait," Claudia began breathlessly.

"Then let's sit here on the step, dear," her mother said. "What is it? You do seem pretty worked up."

"Oh, Mother, listen!" The girl poured out her story on sympathetic and understanding ears. "Please think of something we can do. I feel sure Enid is shielding someone or something. There's a lot I haven't got straight yet, but it's all over Clarksburg High that she was caught stealing hose from the hosiery counter at Sprague's Department Store. The saleslady had been suspicious for some reason and reported it to the store detective. Enid was followed out of the store and the arrest was made. Enid wouldn't say a word in self-defense. They found a pair of hose in her pocket, but my heart tells me that they have made some horrible mistake. Mother, she's innocent. I just know she is. What can we do? You always have the answer."

"I don't know, dear. If you could get her over here I might talk to her."

Mrs. Jeffries' gray eyes wore a puzzled frown. "She surely does need a close friend to counsel her. With no mother, and a father who's away from home on business so much of the time, she must be perplexed. Surely there's a way." She looked up at Claudia who restlessly paced the porch. "Let's ask God to direct us, dear."

The worried girl sat down beside her mother and bowed her head. Except for the chirping of birds as they went about their busy tasks it was very quiet and peaceful in the Jeffries' yard. Then Mrs. Jeffries stood up. "Come on, we are going over there."

"But, Mother, you're in your old garden sweater and there's dry dirt on your hands and your head is tied up in that old red scarf."

"I know, dear, but there's no time to change. We'll take the shortcuts. It is what God wants us to do, I am sure."

They covered the several blocks between the two homes with lightning speed. Claudia and her mother laughed later at the spectacle they must have made. In fact, a neighbor out in her yard had called, "Where's the fire?" but they had only smiled and hurried on. Soon they stood at the door of the Carson home, trying to get their breath as they waited.

Marilyn, the housekeeper, answered their ring.

"May I see Enid, Marilyn?" asked Mrs. Jeffries.

"I don't exactly know." Marilyn hesitated. Her face looked troubled.

"Is she in her room, Marilyn?" Claudia asked.

"Yes, but . . ."

"Then I'll go right up," Mrs. Jeffries interrupted, stepping in front of her and into the house. "Enid is in trouble, Marilyn, and I am going to try to help her. You stay down here until I call you, dear" she added, turning to her daughter.

Claudia watched her mother climb the stairs. Then she patted Marilyn on the shoulder. "Mother is wonderful. She'll get things all straightened out."

"I hope so. I surely do." Marilyn was wiping her eyes with the corner of her blue-checked apron. "I don't know what's wrong but something most certainly is. 'Scuse me, Miss. I better get back to the kitchen."

As Claudia sat in the Carson living room, ears alert for her mother's call, she watched the bright, shiny hands of the big grandfather clock in the corner. They're moving too fast, she thought. Then she thought of other times in her life when she had watched clocks and the hands seemed hardly to move at all. For instance, there was the time her father had been very ill and the doctor had explained solemnly, "Another hour and he will have passed the crisis." That sixty minutes had seemed an eternity to her, her twin brother Bill, and her mother who were waiting at his side. And then there were happy occasions like the day of her first birthday party. She had just learned to tell time and her mother had explained to her and Bill that when the small hand was at two the guests would arrive. Time had lagged along like a little boy not wanting to go into the house from play. But now so much depended on whether there was time for her mother to get close to Enid and get to the bottom of this trouble before the paper went to press. "Maybe if I pray," she said to herself. "Oh, dear God. Please help mother to get it all worked out. I'll be so very thankful."

Just as Claudia finished her prayer she heard her mother coming down the stairs and calling. She burst into the room excitedly. "Go to her, dear. It's all going to be all right. I have some telephoning to do."

"To the paper, Mother?" Claudia was halfway up the stairs.

"Yes, and to Sprague's Department Store. Run along now. Enid is waiting."

And so it was that a girl's good name was kept intact. The paper carried a spicy editorial that evening for the benefit of those who had been hasty in judgment and for others who were so cowardly that they let others take blame for something they, too, had been a party to. Most of the citizens of the little town were unaware, however, that tragedy had passed them by, tragedy in the form of gossip and unjust accusations.

As the two girls sat clasped in each other's arms up in Enid's cheery bedroom, laughing and crying at the same time, Enid exclaimed, "Your mother is wonderful, Claudia. It was so easy to tell her how it all happened. It was just like confiding in my own mother, the mother I never knew."

"But what happened, Enid? Tell me before I explode!"

"Oh, you don't know, do you? And you had such faith in me. When we met on the library steps I wanted to tell you but I thought I was duty bound to keep still. Your mother helped me to think straight."

"Enid Carson, if you don't start clearing up my befuddled head it's going to pop open!"

"I don't believe there is such a word, Claudia," Enid laughed, "but . . ."

"All right, muddled then. Anyway, duty bound to whom? What do you mean?"

"Well, look, Claudia. You know that girls' club I recently joined?"

"That culture club?"

"Yes. Well, there's an initiation that goes with it and, as your mother says, sometimes when girls put their heads together they can conjure up some pretty foolish things. Are you following me?"

"Do you mean . . . ?"

"Yes. Pretending to take those hose was just a silly stunt. I didn't really steal any hose. Those were my own that they found in my pocket. I had bought them with my very own money. I even had the receipt. Oh, why I ever got myself into such a mess is more than I'll ever understand."

"And why didn't you explain it all?"

"That was a part of the silly pledge I had taken, don't you see? I didn't dare involve the girls."

"No, I don't see. So that's culture and friendship, is it?" Claudia's tone was one of disgust.

"I know," sighed Enid. "I can see how utterly silly and dangerous it all was, but I thought I was doing right. With Daddy gone most of the time and no one but Marilyn, as good as she is, I just got all mixed up." She wiped her eyes. "Your mother is going to be my mom, too, from now on . . . that is, if you don't mind our being sisters."

"Mind? I'm tickled pink." Claudia squeezed Enid and they laughed together. "But hold on, Enid. I, Mrs. Sherlock Holmes, have one more question. How did you happen to be in the library this afternoon? I would have thought . . . well . . ."

"I know. Well, I was reading the story over."

"What story?"

"Oh, that's right. I didn't tell you. The girls had found the idea for the stunt from a story. I was reading it over to see where I had slipped up. It just didn't work out the way we intended at all."

"Huh. I could write a better story than that myself. Well, anyway, it's all straightened out now. I saw a story, too, this afternoon. All I read was the title but it made quite an impression on me."

"What was it, Claudia?"

" 'Fair-weather Friends.' I decided, Enid, that I wanted to be more than a fair-weather friend."

"You were a friend, Claudia. And don't forget, we're sisters, too. Come, let's go downstairs."

Mrs. Jeffries and Marilyn stood at the bottom of the steps. The four were soon in a huddle, too happy and excited to speak. But finally Marilyn broke loose. "Well, I do declare, I am the happiest person in the whole, wide world, just seeing my darlin' smilin' again."

"Everything is all right now, Marilyn," Enid explained, hugging her again, "thanks to Mrs. Jeffries and Claudia."

"Thanks to God, dear," added Mrs. Jeffries as she and Claudia started for the door. "Good-bye, and come over any time."

" 'Bye, sis," Claudia added.

As they headed for home Mrs. Jeffries looked down at herself and laughed. "Goodness, I do look a sight, don't I?"

"You look beautiful, Mother, positively beautiful," Claudia assured her, as she put her arm around her.

66

CLAUDIA MAKES A SPEECH

Claudia Jeffries, in her turquoise blue jumper and soft pink blouse, with her hair becomingly tied back, felt that she was now ready to give her talk before the assembly at Clarksburg High School.

That was not all the preparation she had made either. The night before she had said to her mother, "Oh, I know my knees will knock so that everybody can hear them. How can I ever stand before the mob of students and teachers and tell them the history of our church?" She had been thinking of one girl in particular, Betty French, who had more than once said unkind things about her beliefs.

"There is nothing to fear, dear," her mother had assured her. "Wear your prettiest dress, see that you are well groomed, and then forget all about yourself and think of what a good chance you are having to set so many straight on our church. And remember, Claudia, God will be with you."

Claudia had answered, "It is a break, isn't it? It's simply awful, how garbled some people get things. Oh, if they only knew the truth!"

"And you're just the person to tell them," her twin

brother Bill had interrupted, coming into the living room where Claudia and her mother were in conversation. "Ardis and I'll be there pulling for you." Ardis Moore was Claudia's best friend and also a member of her church. Bill and Ardis were together a great deal, too. He stretched out on the divan as his mother added, "And praying for her, too, I hope."

Bill grinned. "That's what I mean, Mom."

The Jeffries family were very loyal to their church. They liked to tell others about the great Restoration movement, and when Claudia had been given the privilege of selecting her own subject for the talk she was scheduled to give in assembly as a part of her course in speech class she had discussed it with her family. Her parents and Bill had agreed that it was too good an opportunity to pass up and helped her each night until she had felt sure of what she wanted to say.

And now the great moment had arrived. Two other students sat on the stage with her. She was in the middle which indicated that she would be the second one to speak. Claudia looked out upon the sea of faces. The Clarksburg High School student body had never looked so large nor the faculty row so imposing. She could see Bill and Ardis on the front row. Not far from them was Fred Sears, the boy whom she especially liked and who was becoming quite interested in the church. He had gone with her to a number of Zion's League meetings.

"But who is that beside him?" pondered Claudia, frowning in spite of herself as she noticed him talking to an attractive red-haired girl. "I've never seen her before." For a moment Claudia had an uncomfortable feeling. "You silly," she scolded herself. "Act your age." She enjoyed Fred's company a lot and had been thrilled that he seemed to like her and her church. Claudia, however, forced herself to put this aside in her thinking as she heard the first speaker being introduced. The girl's talk which had to do with the raising of orchids, a hobby of her father's, was very well presented and when she had finished she walked assuredly back to her seat. And then Claudia heard her name called and she took her place in the center of the stage. Very simply, with a prayer in her heart, she announced her subject and gave her reason for selecting it. A quietness that was almost frightening settled over the auditorium. Although her face reflected composure Claudia's heart was pounding and then, remembering that God was with her, she began her talk. Ideas and ways of bringing her church to this large body came to her mind in an almost miraculous way. She knew God was blessing her. It was hard to stop when her time was up.

As the third speaker, a boy, was announced and went into his speech on the subject of atom bombs, Claudia tried to listen, but in spite of herself her mind would wander momentarily. She was hoping those who had heard her now saw her church with clearer vision.

After assembly Claudia's closest friends gathered around her. Bill and Ardis were pumping her hands and patting her on the back and Fred, with the redhead at his side, was pushing his way through the crowd.

"Claud, you were terrific!" he exclaimed.

"Thanks, Fred." Claudia smiled happily and there were tears in her eyes as she thought that the way he spoke everything was much the same between them. She started to remark that God was with her when Fred went on, "Look, I want you girls to meet." He linked his arm through that of the girl standing beside him. "Claudia, this is my cousin Donna who just got in from Chicago this morning. Donna,

I want you to meet the nicest girl in Clarksburg." Claudia blushed. "I'm happy to meet you, Donna," she said, and to herself added, "and to learn the relationship between you two."

The bells were ringing for classes and the gang broke up but not before Claudia had invited Donna and Fred to the campfire meeting the Zion's League was having the following night.

As she and Ardis walked along to English class together her friend sighed contentedly, "Claudia, you gave us such a beautiful picture of our church. I appreciate it more than ever now."

"And so do I, Ardis," agreed Claudia. "Oh, it was a wonderful experience, one I hope I shall never forget. Why, God even put words in my mouth."

All that day different ones, students and teachers, expressed their interest in her speech. Several said they would like to hear more and one teacher asked for literature to read; and then when Betty French came up with tears in her eyes and said, "Forgive me, Claudia, please, for all the unkind things I've said about you and your church," Claudia knew that she was the happiest girl in the world. She put her arm around her newfound friend and said, "I knew you didn't realize, Betty." She invited Betty home to stay all night with her. Betty accepted, humbly explaining that she had been prejudiced by someone who really did not know the facts as Claudia had presented them.

"That happens more often than I like to admit," offered Claudia. "Maybe someday everyone will know. I surely hope so."

The girls talked half the night about the church. Claudia told Betty all about Graceland College, the Sanitarium where so many church girls receive their nurse's training, reunions, youth camps, and many other phases of her church life.

"It all sounds so fascinating," exclaimed Betty. "I want to learn more and more. How I'd like to go to Graceland and to take nurse's training at the San." Claudia knew that Betty had planned to be a nurse. "I know now that the things I've heard and repeated were not true; I'd like to give my life to helping others know the truth as you have helped me." Claudia knew that Betty was sincere, too, for there was a ring of honesty in her voice and her face was radiant.

When Mrs. Jeffries gently tapped at the door, reminding them that it was almost one o'clock and that there was school the next day Claudia answered back softly, "Okay, Mother." She turned off the bed lamp and two completely happy girls reluctantly bade each other good-night.

But Claudia did not go to sleep immediately. This was her first chance to be alone with herself and God.

"Thank you, dear Father," she prayed silently, "for putting it into my heart to talk about your church of the latter days. Thank you for helping me to say the right things. And I do want to thank you so very much for Betty who is eager to know more. May nothing hinder this desire." Claudia prayed for other friends whom she and Ardis and Bill might interest if they but kept their own lives shining with the light of Christ. She thought of Fred and his cousin, Donna. Why, if Fred learns what a wonderful thing it is he will share it with Donna, thought Claudia, and for the first time she saw with clearer understanding the far-reaching effects of sharing the gospel.

She was so thankful and so happy for all her blessings and opportunities that her heart was almost bursting. With a "Thank you, God, for everything," she curled up into a compact ball and went happily to sleep.

67

MEDICINE FOR THE DOCTOR

"Dad, are you acquainted with Dr. French, Betty's father?" Claudia put the question as the Jeffries sat at the breakfast table. The morning sunshine filtered through the white, dotted-swiss curtains at the windows, bringing out the rich blue of the willowware.

Her father looked up from his cereal. "Yes, slightly." Then he questioned guardedly, "Why do you ask?"

"Well, look, Dad. Is it true that he drinks quite a bit?"

Claudia's mother interrupted. "Where did you hear that, dear? I hope you haven't been gossiping."

Her twin brother, Bill, appeared interested, too. "If that's so, no wonder Betty is here so much these days. She probably wants to get away from it."

"Bill!" spoke up Mrs. Jeffries rather sharply. "Let's not reach conclusions too hastily."

Claudia sighed. "I'm afraid it's true and I'm not bringing this up in a gossipy way either. Poor Betty. We've become such good friends, you know, and she seems to love to talk about the church with me. One day, though, when we were discussing the use of tobacco and liquor she said, 'Well, I can put up with my father's smoking but' . . . and then she clapped her hand over her mouth just as if she had almost betrayed him. I felt so sorry for her."

Mr. Jeffries wiped his mouth on his napkin and pushed his chair back from the table. His eyes were serious. "Yes," he admitted, "it is common knowledge among the business and professional men about town that Dr. French has been drinking pretty steadily these days. It's a pity, since he was one of the finest physicians in Clarksburg. But many so-called moderns see no harm in drinking. The cocktail is as ordinary in their homes as fruit juices in ours. Too bad, for it always spells trouble. Yes, it always spells trouble with a capital T."

Lack of time prevented further discussion as breakfast was finished and a busy day lay ahead for each of them. The Jeffries family always followed a certain pattern, however, so after having had the *Daily Bread* reading, they sang the suggested hymn together around the piano and then knelt for prayer. Each one remembered Betty's father that morning, praying that he might see his mistake before it was too late.

It was two weeks later that a series of missionary services was begun. Elder Compton, the guest speaker, urged all the members to invite their friends and neighbors. Members of the Zion's League were having a contest to see how many nonmembers they could get to attend, and Claudia, naturally, asked Betty and her parents. Dr. French rebelled. "I'm no church man," he grumbled to Betty when she approached him.

Later she again asked him. Unfortunately he had been drinking and his disposition was ugly. "If you think you are going to get me to that church you had better just change your mind!" he stormed, throwing down the evening paper angrily and stomping up the stairs. Betty cried herself to sleep.

One night, however, as Betty and her parents were returning home from a movie Betty felt that her father was in quite an amiable mood and again ventured to mention the missionary meetings.

"I'll see, Pudge," he answered good-naturedly. Betty went to sleep that night with a song in her heart, and the next day as she and Claudia were walking home from school she told her friend of her father's halfway promise. "Whenever he calls me 'Pudge' I know he's in a pretty good frame of mind," Betty exclaimed. "He has called me by that pet name ever since I was a little girl. Oh, Claudia, I may as well tell you about Dad."

"Don't, Betty, if you'd rather not," protested Claudia.

"I want to, for we need your prayers."

It was hard for her but finally the story was out. "He's as good a father as a girl could possibly have when he isn't drinking," she began, "but when one of these spells comes on he's like a stranger to us. Mother and I have both begged him to quit, to join Alcoholics Anonymous or to do something, but he won't listen to us." Her eyes were bright with tears.

"Something will work out," Claudia comforted her as the girls parted a few minutes later. When she saw the French family at church the following Sunday night she felt as if her heart would burst, for she knew prayers had borne fruit. They were a handsome family. Dr. French's

226

prematurely gray hair glistened. He was faultlessly attired. Mrs. French, a little woman, was trim in a neat blue suit and becoming hat. Claudia noticed how proudly Betty walked down the aisle with them as they were ushered to their seats.

Elder Compton, the missionary, preached a sermon that Claudia felt was another answer to prayer. In a forceful yet gentle manner, he presented his message, using "He Came to Himself" for his subject. For his scripture he read the story of the prodigal son, and his development of it kept the congregation entranced. Betty's father sat much of the time with bowed head. Claudia prayed more earnestly than she had ever prayed in her life. "He's a good man," she petitioned. "He would make a wonderful helper in your kingdom. I know you love him even as the father in the story. I do pray that he will feel that love." Her eyes were wet as she stood up with the others to sing the closing hymn. After the benediction was pronounced, Claudia looked for Betty in the foyer.

"Daddy's talking with Elder Compton in the pastor's study," Betty whispered. "Oh, Claudia, pray hard."

Claudia was thrilled. She would have been even more so could she have sat in on that conversation.

"Elder Compton," Betty's father began, "you made me think tonight. I believe for the first time I am ready to try to overcome a habit that is gradually—perhaps not so gradually at that—leading me straight to the pigsty. It is ruining my own life and causing much unhappiness in the lives of my wife and daughter. I need your medicine, the kind of medicine that will help me to overcome this awful habit of drink."

Betty and her mother sat in the car for thirty minutes waiting after everyone else had gone home, but when Dr.

French came out they noticed he walked with a spring. He said nothing, however, except to ask if they would like ice-cream cones on the way home.

The next day at school Betty ran up to Claudia with shining eyes. She burst out excitedly, "Oh, Claudia, I don't know what happened but something surely did. For the first time in my life I saw Dad reading the Bible and I heard him muttering something about 'licking this thing' and 'medicine for the doctor.' I know something wonderful has happened. I'm so happy I could sing!"

The French family was in attendance at church regularly after this. Then one Sunday night just as Claudia and her family were leaving the house the telephone rang.

"I'll get it," Claudia called. It was Betty. "Oh, no!" cried Claudia into the mouthpiece. When she hung the receiver back on the hook her face was pale and tears ran down her cheeks. "It's Dr. French," she sobbed. "He has been drinking again and there was an accident in a car. He's in the hospital, seriously hurt. Oh, why did this have to happen?"

All during the service she groped for the answer to her question. Help came in Elder Compton's closing remarks as he reminded his listeners of the great forgiving nature of God. "He has given us our agency and sometimes we use it self-destructively instead of to his glory. But he looks down upon us much as we do upon the little child who is learning to walk. The toddler takes his tumbles now and then but we help him up so that he may try again. We do this because we love him and want to help. Yes, God's love is like that, all-encompassing. He is so kind and patient with us, his faltering children." Peace came to Claudia's heart. "Why, Dr. French is like the little child who is learning to walk. We must be patient and help him to try again." Stopping at the French home on her way to school the next morning she told Betty of what had come to her.

"He's awfully discouraged," Betty replied. "I think he feels as if he hasn't the right now to any recognition from God."

"You must tell him, Betty," insisted Claudia. "Tell him just what I have told you." Betty promised.

The doctor's life hung by a thread for several days. A special prayer service was held for him at the church. Elder Compton and the local pastor visited him and explained the ordinance of administration. After some persuasion on the part of his wife and daughter he asked to be administered to. There was no immediate healing, but Dr. French's spiritual health took a turn for the better. In a few days he was able to leave the hospital and begin his long recuperation at home. Claudia and her family made frequent calls. Tasty delicacies were brought in by friends and neighbors. The church books and *Heralds* found their way to the sick man's bedside and he read for himself the story of Christ's church restored in the latter days. With his family he read the Book of Mormon and was enthralled with its message; he even planned a month's vacation for the following summer in Mexico and Central America. One evening as he and Mr. Jeffries talked while the women and girls were visiting in another part of the house, Dr. French said laconically, "You know, I'm almost glad this all happened. It has given me time to diagnose my case. I know I needed the treatment that Elder Compton prescribed. I'll need a lot of that kind of medicine, many doses of prayer, large amounts of study of the word of God, and much spiritual exercise. Yes, I think I can say that I have 'come to myself.' "

"Why, he talks about it morning, noon, and night," Betty confided to Claudia as they were leaving a Zion's League meeting. Eventually she and her parents were again attending church. Then on the night of the missionary's farewell sermon he announced in closing that there were several candidates for baptism. "If there are others," he concluded, "I'll be happy to add your names to the list."

Dr. French stood up. Falteringly at first and then gradually with more steadiness of speech he asked if he might say a few words. "Certainly, Doctor," Elder Compton nodded.

A spirit of expectancy hovered over the congregation.

"I am here tonight," began Dr. French, "as a result of your prayers and God's great forgiving love for the sinner. I had never known how great that love really is until I came in contact with this church of the latter days and you people, but *now I know* and I feel I should like to give all I have in God's service. My wife and daughter are ready for baptism and I know nothing would make them happier than to see our family united in this adventure. I am a physician. I was a good one until I let liquor take hold of me. I have worked with God, though I did not comprehend to what extent, in bringing health to many. Now I am in need of that Great Physician if I am to keep the fine resolves of my heart. If you are willing to accept me as your brother, weak but wanting to become strong, I shall be happy to enter my name for baptism."

As Dr. French sat down the organist began playing "Blest Be the Tie That Binds" and after the congregation had sung it with deep feeling Elder Compton pronounced the benediction. With silent reverence the congregation left the sanctuary. It was just as if each one present knew he had walked with God.

68

IT WAS MOTHER'S IDEA

Claudia Jeffries and her family were spending the night at home. This was not an unusual practice for them, for just a year before they had come to a very important decision. Mrs. Jeffries had been the instigator. One evening at the dinner table her husband had hardly spoken a word because he was intent upon eating and getting off to a meeting; her son Bill was practically swallowing his food whole to leave for basketball practice; and Claudia had choir coming up in less than an hour. It was then she had dropped the bomb, so to speak.

"There's going to be a change around this house," she exclaimed.

Mr. Jeffries looked up from his plate, his fork in mid-air. "Now, Mother, don't tell me you're having one of those moving moods again. Why, the last time you switched the furniture I had an awful time finding my way around."

Claudia and Bill laughed. "Now, Dad," offered Claudia, "you know it wasn't that bad."

Bill agreed with his father. "I know what he means. I like to see things in their places, if you ask me."

"How about those pajamas and socks I picked up in your room this morning?" asked Claudia, with a grin.

"I consider myself squelched," sighed Bill, with an air of mock martyrdom.

Mrs. Jeffries listened to the jesting but was not going to be sidetracked. Claudia could see that as she looked into her mother's serious countenance.

"Just what *do* you mean, Mother?" she questioned.

Her mother smiled. "I'll explain. Do you know that for the past three weeks we haven't had one single night when all of us have been at home together? And it can't go on. I mean it. It can't go on! We've got to have an evening together now and then or we're going to fail—as a family, that is."

The others were speechless. It wasn't often that Mother became so emphatic. Finally, a bit meekly, Mr. Jeffries asked, "Just what do you propose, Mother? Locking the door and throwing away the key?"

"Mother's got a point, Dad, a very good one," put in Claudia. "Why, in our homemaking class just the other day we learned that every family should have one night a week together, a night when they get better acquainted with each other through uninterrupted visiting and doing things as a family—and, well, when *have* we had a night alone? Yes, Mother has something."

"But everything we do is *important*," Bill insisted. "We're not wasting our time."

"Bill's right," agreed Mr. Jeffries. "There are nights when I'd like to sit by the fireside, I'll admit." He turned to his wife as though asking her to understand. Claudia could see the look of disappointment that came to her

232

mother's face. She started to speak but her father continued.

"Have you decided on the night, Mother?"

"No, that is something we must all work out together. And we're going to do it right now. The dishes and other things can wait."

Mr. Jeffries looked hastily at his watch. Bill did likewise. Claudia knew she had time.

"I can give it half an hour," said Bill. "How about you, Dad?"

"Why, certainly," he agreed.

"Shall we go into the living room?" suggested Mrs. Jeffries. As the four entered the softly lighted room Claudia breathed a short prayer. She sensed that her mother was praying, too. It wasn't that her father and brother weren't the best in the world, but she knew how very seriously they took their obligations. She admired them with all her heart and knew her mother was proud of them, too, but still she felt her mother had started something that was very important. As each found his favorite chair she said to herself, "Yes, we do need this. There's too much tension around this house."

"We'll do this by the process of elimination," Mrs. Jeffries explained.

"That's what I thought," said Bill, "and in my own thinking I've eliminated them all."

His mother ignored him. "Let's start with Monday," she suggested.

"Why, Monday is always the night I go priesthood calling," put in Mr. Jeffries. "Surely you can't expect me to give that up."

"No, dear." His wife smiled patiently. "It's also Bill's night with his Cubs. Monday is definitely out."

233

"And Tuesday night Dad and I work at the store," Bill offered. Mr. Jeffries was the owner and manager of a thriving grocery business which he operated with the able assistance of his son.

"Yes, Tuesday is out," admitted Mrs. Jeffries. Claudia was thinking of what she did on Tuesday nights. She and eleven other girls, some nonmembers, were in a club that had been recently organized for the purpose of improving their talents in the interests of the church. With a sigh of relief she said to herself, "I'm glad I don't have to give that up." The she heard her mother say, "We know we can't take Wednesday night, for that is prayer meeting and so now we come to Thursday."

"But that is your night," the three shouted. For years Mrs. Jeffries had used Thursday afternoon and evening as her time off. Sometimes she went friendly visiting. Sometimes there were women's meetings, committees, and the like. No, they couldn't let her give that up.

"And there's Friday," she went on. "That's recreation night and I wouldn't ask that of you. Besides, Dad and I enjoy that night, too, to be alone or do whatever we please." Claudia looked at her mother with a feeling of pity and frustration. What are we going to do? she thought. There's only Saturday night left and, well, that's as good as no night at all. We can't make a family night out of that with all the things we do. Of course, we're usually all home, but we're all so occupied with our own responsibilities. Poor Mother. Her plan has failed even before she has begun it. She felt like crying when of a sudden she came to with a start. Her mother was saying, "So that leaves Saturday. It will just have to be Saturday."

"But, my dear!" That was Claudia's father.

"But, Mother!" Claudia and Bill added.

"Oh, we can do it; that is, if we want to enough. What do we do on Saturday nights? Usually the things that we should have done earlier in the day or week. Now be honest." Mother smiled to soften the blow.

Claudia was thinking hard, and she knew that her father and Bill were, too. What did she do with her Saturday nights? Once in a while she had a date. Ordinarily she washed and pinned her hair, worked on her lesson, pressed some clothes, or made a batch of fudge. There were numerous things she did that could have been taken care of at some other time just as well. It was the same with Bill and her father. Sometimes they stayed down at the store long after closing time just talking shop and when they did come home they wasted a perfectly good two hours or more fussing around with things they could have done earlier in the week had there been better planning. Yes, thought Claudia, it could be Saturday night. Even Mother could organize a bit better so she wouldn't need to be starting to bake a cake at nine-thirty at night!

Deep in their thoughts, they almost jumped when Mrs. Jeffries asked quietly, "Have you thought it over? Are you going to give it a try?"

As Claudia was talking it over later with her mother she said, "How could we let you down?"

Consequently, on the following Saturday night the new plan was inaugurated. At first they hardly knew how to act. How well Claudia remembered that Bill had asked, "What are we supposed to do?" Their mother had answered, "We're going to enjoy each other. That's one thing. Another thing, we're going to learn the almost lost art of conversation. When have we, as a family, had an evening just to ourselves, to do with as we pleased? We'll have picnics, we'll talk over our problems, we'll decide major issues that concern all of us. We'll help each other. You just wait and see. The time will go quickly. You won't be bored."

Bill had looked doubtful but strangely enough they weren't bored. It was a wonderful feeling just to relax, knowing that you could spend the entire evening that way and not suddenly have to jump up and go somewhere.

One evening Bill presented a problem.

"They're calling me a sissy because I go to church so much. The fellows say that it is all right to go in the morning once in a while but only old people go at night. And prayer meeting! Well, they poke fun at me until I can hardly stand it." For months Bill had been carrying this resentment around inside him and what a relief it had been to talk it over with the family and get a different attitude. "You know," he had confessed, "I never could have had this out with you before we started these meetings."

The family had to laugh. "Meetings. Yes, they are meetings in a way," Mr. Jeffries had said. "And I, for one, am plenty thankful that Mother saw our need. I know you have all helped me more than once. Working for the public for a good many years, a fellow is apt to get soured once in a while; but with you all here to talk things over with me, I'm a better storekeeper, a better minister, and a better man. It's—it's—wonderful!"

No wonder then that on the year commemorating the date of their new adventure in family sharing they felt they should do something extra special. Most of their get-togethers had closed with the family singing a hymn or two followed by individual prayers, but this one was to be planned with added care. They discussed some of the highlights of their year and with great humility realized that much had been accomplished. When Mr. Jeffries needed some extra money to branch out in his business the family knew about it and with loving cooperation made it possible. When Mrs. Jeffries explained her physical condition, after a doctor's checkup, she shared it with her family instead of trying to carry the load alone. How much closer it had brought them! This was an occasion of great importance.

As it developed, the family realized it was very much like one of their prayer meetings at church, with testimonies and all. Mr. Jeffries summed it all up very nicely when he said, "This idea of yours has done us more good, Mother, than any one thing that ever happened to our family. It has united us. Why, we could meet anything that might happen now—all because we have come to know each other better. How I wish every family might know the value of this!" In full agreement the others nodded their heads and Bill exclaimed, "God bless Mother."

69

CHET THE PAPER BOY

It was the darkest fall night imaginable. The wind was blowing about Chet, the paper boy, tugging at his hat and flapping his pants legs. As he turned the corner, he exclaimed, "One more stop and then I can go home. Boy, will I be glad to get in that warm house. I'm hungry, too, and Mom is sure to have something good to eat." Just then he noticed that there was no light in the house he was approaching.

Why, Widow Brown must not be home, he thought. I wonder if she has gone to visit her son. Maybe I ought to pass her house by tonight. No use leaving a paper at a dark house. I can drop it there in the morning.

In his heart Chet knew he should deliver the paper, however, so he hurried on, going up the steps of the porch to place it beneath the rock beside the door. Just then as he turned away he heard, through the noise of the whistling wind, someone calling, "Help, help!" Chet was frightened. He knew Mrs. Brown lived alone. He said to himself, "Something has happened. She must have fallen or . . . or . . ."

He pushed at the door but it was locked. Again he heard her call.

"Help, help!"

Chet ran through the darkness to the back door. It, too, was locked and would not budge.

I know, thought the boy, and he lifted himself up to the kitchen window.

"Oh, thank goodness," he exclaimed, raising it high enough to get in. He lowered himself into the room and called softly, "Mrs. Brown. It's Chet, your paper boy. Where are you?"

"Here in the living room, son," came back the feeble answer. "Thank God, you heard."

"Where is the light, Mrs. Brown?" Chet called again, feeling his way along. "Oh, I found it!" With darkness gone the boy could see the old woman lying upon the floor. A cut was on her forehead. For a minute Chet felt helpless. Then fortunately words he had memorized from the Bible came to him. "I will trust and not be afraid." He knew God was depending upon him and, lifting the woman gently, he almost carried her to the couch. When she was resting comfortably, Chet hurried to the kitchen for warm water to bathe her head and also brought her a cool drink. All the while Mrs. Brown kept repeating, "Bless you, my boy, bless you."

Chet patted her tenderly on the shoulder, and said, "I'm so glad I heard you. I'm going to call Mother, and I know she and Dad will be right over. My dad is a doctor, you know, and a minister, too."

While they waited Mrs. Brown explained her accident. "A dizziness must have come over me," she said. "I fell, hitting my head on the table. I think I fainted. I had been lying there for a good while. I couldn't get up so I prayed. Oh, my boy, you are the answer to those prayers."

Chet stirred up the fire in the heater and just then he heard a car drive up. He knew his mother and father had come and how thankful he was. Soon his father had dressed the wound, and his mother was feeding Mrs. Brown warm chicken soup she had brought along. "There's some for you, too, Chet," she smiled, handing him a big bowlful.

"Um-m, is this ever good!" exclaimed the boy.

When they had finished, the old woman said, "Doctor, your boy has told me a lot about your church since he has been delivering my paper."

"And he has told us a lot about your cookies, too," laughed the doctor.

"Yes, we've had good visits," she said, and smiled. "And one day he told me about the elders of your church administering to the sick. I wonder—if—if—"

"You mean you'd like to be administered to?" questioned Chet's father. "Why, of course, Mrs. Brown."

Chet and his mother joined silently in the petition for Mrs. Brown's welfare, and Chet, the paper boy, felt a warm gladness steal into his heart.

70

ELLEN
THE MONEY
CHANGER

"I want that pretty girl to wait upon me," said Mr. Brown as he walked into Jones Grocery Store. He pointed right at Ellen, who was putting cans of corn on the shelves. Ellen turned around happily. She was neatly dressed in a jumper of green corduroy and a spotless white blouse. Her red hair lay in soft curls.

"What may I do for you, Mr. Brown?" she asked.

"Well, sir, or miss I should say, here's the list. Mrs. Brown doesn't trust me to remember."

Ellen took the piece of paper and began putting up the order . . . a dozen eggs, a box of oatmeal, a can of salmon, potatoes. Mr. Brown, her customer, walked over to the desk where Ellen's father sat working on his books. Mr. Jones looked up and smiled.

"She's quite a saleslady, isn't she?" he asked.

"Can't beat her," agreed Mr. Brown. "Why, she acts as if she really enjoys it. Too many youngsters seem to be allergic to work. It's a joy to watch her. You're lucky, Pete."

The two men talked of other things and then Mr. Brown turned back to the smiling girl. "How about taking home some of these delicious apples, Mr. Brown? They're our special today. Surprise Mrs. Brown."

The man scrutinized the price. "Sounds fair and they do look good. Give me about fifty cents' worth. We'll try them first and if they're good I'll come back for more."

Ellen weighed them up and totaled the bill and after Mr. Brown had paid for the groceries he left the store with a cheery "Come again, Mr. Brown," ringing in his ears.

Mr. Brown was whistling as he walked into the kitchen of his home. "Grocery boy!" he called, and his wife, a stout little woman in a neat blue housedress, greeted him with a smile.

"Did Ellen wait on you?" she asked.

"That she did, and right smart girl she is, too. Why, she broke that ten-dollar bill and gave me change just as easily as if she had been doing it for years."

Mrs. Brown had a puzzled look. "Ten-dollar bill?" she queried. "Why, Bob, we didn't have a ten-dollar bill. Don't you remember? We both talked about the twenty being our all until the first of the month. We spoke of keeping within our allowance, you know." Mr. Brown was a retired missionary for the church, and he and Mrs. Brown were very careful stewards.

Mr. Brown turned pale. "You're right, Mother. Ellen and I must have made a mistake. Though I just can't believe she could have done such a thing. She's so careful. I'll go to the phone and call her."

Ellen answered. "Jones Grocery. May I help you, please? Oh, yes, Mr. Brown. What? Why, yes, I remember. You gave me a ten-dollar bill."

242

Mr. Brown explained about the twenty.

"I don't see how I could have done it," said Ellen, "but you come into the store and my father will take care of it for you. Thank you for calling." She managed to keep her voice steady until she had hung up the phone, and then she went weeping to her father.

"Why, what is the matter with my favorite saleslady?" he asked as she threw her arms around his neck and sobbed unhappily.

Ellen explained. Her father listened carefully. "And you trusted me, Daddy, and now you'll not want me here any more."

"Now, honey, you just dry those pretty brown eyes and listen to me." He drew a big white handkerchief from his pocket. "Here, blow your nose, too."

Ellen felt better at once. "Now, listen," began her father. "There just isn't anyone in the world who doesn't make mistakes sometimes. But I have a hunch that this wasn't your mistake. I think it will be cleared up. You're always so careful. What do you say we ask God to help us?" Ellen's father was a storekeeper, but he was also a minister in Jesus' church and he served God in many ways. "Let's just bow our heads, Ellen, and talk to God about it before someone comes in."

The click of the screen door announcing a customer came just as Mr. Jones said, "Amen."

"Thank you, Dad," whispered Ellen as she left to wait upon the little boy who had come in.

All that afternoon she kept expecting Mr. Brown. She did not know how their prayers would be answered, but there was a feeling in her heart that all would be well. And then just at closing time Mr. Brown walked in. His face was wreathed in smiles.

"Ellen, forgive me, please, for doubting your efficiency as a money changer. I kept saying to Mrs. Brown, 'There's some explanation. Ellen is so careful.' And I waited and waited, hoping the answer would come. And it did, Ellen."

"Please tell us, Bob," said Ellen's father as he turned from the cash register where he had been counting the money taken in for the day. "We came out within a few cents of being even. I knew there had to be an answer." Ellen waited almost breathlessly.

"You see," explained Mr. Brown, "my wife was so sure that I gave you a twenty-dollar bill that I thought I did, too. I never once thought that our twenty dollars might have been two tens. All afternoon I thought and thought and thought but never considered looking in my billfold. And then a strange thing happened. I was trying to talk myself into coming down here to collect my other ten dollars when a still small voice seemed to say to me, 'Look in your billfold.' I opened up my billfold and there lay the ten-dollar bill and the change from another ten."

It was a very happy girl who linked her arm through her father's as they started for home.

INDEXES

SUBJECT INDEX

246

Special Themes and Occasions Index